Natural Treasures of the Great Plains

# Natural Treasures
# of the Great Plains

## An Ecological Perspective

*Edited by*
Tom Lynch, Paul A. Johnsgard, and Jack Phillips

Published in partnership with the
Great Plains Ecotourism Coalition

PRAIRIE CHRONICLES PRESS
Lincoln, Nebraska

Published by Prairie Chronicles Press in partnership with the Great Plains Ecotourism Coalition

**PRAIRIE CHRONICLES PRESS**
An imprint of Infusionmedia
140 North 8th Street #214, Lincoln, NE 68508
www.infusion.media

**GREAT PLAINS ECOTOURISM COALITION**
1155 Q Street, Lincoln, NE 68588
www.visittheprairie.com

Map by Katie Nieland
Illustrations by Paul A. Johnsgard
Cover photo by Melissa Borman
Cover and page design by Infusionmedia

ISBN 978-0-9916455-9-6 First Edition May 2015
Library of Congress Control Number: 2015937174

10 9 8 7 6 5 4 3 2 1

# TABLE OF CONTENTS

*Map Key*   ix
*Nebraska Sites of Interest Map*   x

PAUL A. JOHNSGARD
Foreword: In Praise of Prairie Fires and the Lasting Legacies
of the Temporary   xiii
RICHARD EDWARDS
Great Plains Ecotourism Coalition Preface: Can Ecotourism
Help Save the Great Plains?   xxi
TOM LYNCH
Introduction: Mapping the Treasures   xxix

**PART I: People and Places**

HEATHER SARLES PAYNE
The Otoe and Missouria: Four Hundred Years of History   3
ROBERT KELLEY SCHNEIDERS
Buffalo Roads and River Bottoms: Restoring an
Ancient Ecology   7
PAUL A. JOHNSGARD
A Place Called Pahaku   13
MICHAEL FARRELL
Hinterlands   21
PAUL A. JOHNSGARD
Secrets of the Most Sincerely Dead: Agate Fossil Beds
National Monument   33

**DEB ECHO-HAWK AND RONNIE O'BRIEN**
Saving the Pawnee Mother Corn   41
**JOEL SARTORE**
Saving Species, Saving Ourselves   47


**PART II: Grasslands and Savannas**

**MITCH PAINE**
Spring Creek Prairie   55
**TWYLA M. HANSEN**
Prairie: Up Close and Personal   63
**WILLIAM BEACHLY**
Clouds and Concretions   69
**JOHN JANOVY JR.**
Keith County, Nebraska: An Introduction   75
**CHRIS HELZER**
Prairie Diversity   79
**BENJAMIN VOGT**
Why We Need Native Wildflowers   87
**SIBYLLA BROWN**
Restoring Oak Savannas   91


**PART III: Forests, Rivers, and Wetlands**

**JACK PHILLIPS**
On Planting Wildly   99

**LINDA R. BROWN**
The Natural Calendar at Wilderness Park    105

**STEPHEN DINSMORE**
Birding Lake McConaughy    109

**MATT GERSIB**
Escape to the River    117

**TOM LYNCH**
The World Looks Different from the Middle of a Lake    123

**JOANNA POPE**
Wetlands    129


**PART IV: Plants and Animals**


**ALAN J. BARTELS**
The Turtles of Nebraska    139

**CHARLES BROWN**
Swallows along the Platte: What the Cliff Swallows of Western
Nebraska Have Taught Us about Animal Social Life    159

**PAUL A. JOHNSGARD**
The Greater Prairie-chicken: Spirit of the Tallgrass Prairie    171

**GEORGE ARCHIBALD**
The Special Magic of Cranes    177

**PAUL A. JOHNSGARD**
The Allure of Cranes    185

**BENJAMIN VOGT**
Monarch Butterflies: The Last Migration    191

*Acknowledgments*   199
*About the Authors*   201
*About the Great Plains Ecotourism Coalition*   211
Prairie Fire *Chronology*   215

## MAP KEY

1. Great Platte River Road Archway, Buffalo County
2. Kingsley Dam, Keith County
3. Rowe Audubon Sanctuary/Crane Trust, Buffalo County
4. Nature Conservancy's Platte River Prairies, Buffalo and Hall counties
5. Rainwater Basin, between Kearney and Lancaster counties
6. Salt Basin Saline wetlands, Lancaster County
7. Cedar Point Biological Station, Keith County
8. Wilderness Park, Lancaster County
9. Niobrara River Canoe Trail, Cherry to Keya Paha County
10. Calamus River Canoe Trail, Brown, Rock, and Loup counties
11. Republican River Canoe Trail, Harlan to Webster County
12. Fort Robinson State Park, Sioux and Dawes counties
13. The Oglala National Grasslands, Sioux County
14. Chimney Rock, Morrill County
15. Courthouse Rock, Morrill County
16. Devil's Backbone (Wyoming)
17. Boar's Tusk (Wyoming)
18. Spring Creek Prairie Audubon Center, Lancaster County
19. Agate Fossil Beds, Sioux County
20. Hudson-Meng Bison Bone Bed (near Crawford, Nebraska)
21. Pahaku (north of Cedar Bluffs, Nebraska)
22. Timberhill, Decatur County, Iowa
23. Lakes McConaughy and Ogalala, Keith County
24. Olive Creek State Recreation Area, Lancaster County
25. Nine-mile Prairie, Lancaster County
26. Willa Cather Memorial Prairie, Webster County
27. Ashfall Fossil Beds, Antelope County

# Nebraska Sites of Interest

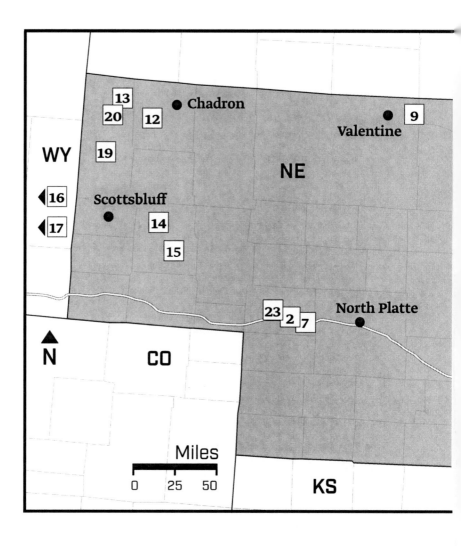

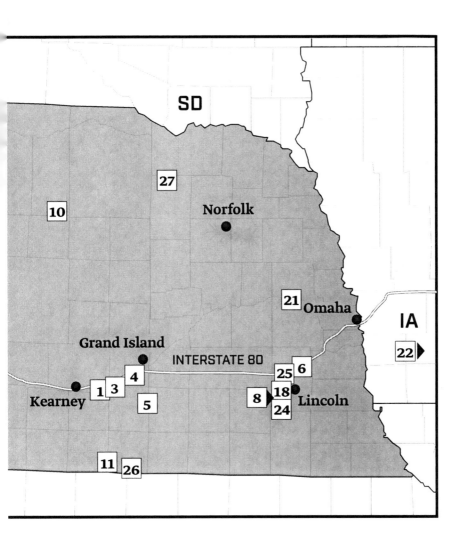

SD

27

10

Norfolk

21 Omaha

IA

22

Grand Island

INTERSTATE 80

25 6

4

1 3

8 18

24

Lincoln

Kearney

5

11

26

Map by Katie Nieland

# In Praise of Prairie Fires and the Lasting Legacies of the Temporary

## PART I

*The face of the earth is a graveyard, and so it has always been.*

—**Paul Sears, 1935**

One of my earliest memories, and one so early and fragmented that I sometimes wonder if it really happened, dates back to about 1935, in the middle of the Great Depression. I was perhaps four years old, and we were living in Christine, then a town of about one hundred people, in North Dakota's Red River Valley. My foggy memory is that my mother awakened me on a warm summer night and that my dad then drove mother, my brother, and me out into the country to watch a prairie fire sweeping across the dry countryside.

A year or two later another uncontrolled fire burned down the only grocery story in Christine. I vividly remember standing across the street and fearfully watching its orange flames ascend high against the nighttime sky. Luckily, nobody was hurt in that blaze, and, in God's infinite wisdom, a nearby saloon was left untouched. However, the disaster meant that Christine's residents would have to drive to a nearby town for many of their day-to-day needs. The event no doubt helped stifle the town's chances for much long-term future growth (Christine still has fewer than 150 residents), but grandfather's general store expanded its inventory to help provide the area's basic needs. His store increasingly became a kind of unofficial meeting place for all the locals. I remember listening in on small groups of men as they sat in a circle on frigid winter days, absorbing the warmth of a pot-bellied stove and exchanging stories and jokes in Norwegian, effectively excluding me from their humor.

Sometimes small fires also broke out along the right-of-way of the railroad line that passed through Christine, perhaps from discarded cigarettes or train sparks, keeping the route in native vegetation. The train tracks provided me with a convenient route to hike during summer. It was there, where red-winged blackbirds nested abundantly in adjacent ditches, wildflowers flourished, and big bluestem grew taller than my head, that I began to appreciate the rich wonders of prairie life.

Since then I have watched lightning-caused wildfires and controlled burns march across grasslands in southeastern Nebraska, the Flint Hills of Kansas, the Platte Valley, and the Nebraska Sandhills. All of them have provided a kind of hypnotic visual attraction; to see large red-cedars suddenly catch fire and explode in flames offers a glimpse of the terror that these events must trigger among the local wildlife. Within hours after the passage of grassland fires, it is common to see buteo hawks and vultures circling overhead; the burn's ashes expose the runways of voles and other rodents, as well as the bodies of those unlucky individuals that were unable to escape.

In the immediate aftermath of a grassland fire all seems hopeless and dead. Yet, in their above-ground destruction, the grasses and other burned vegetation deposit a legacy of the minerals from which they were composed. These minerals offer a rich fertilizing bounty for the seeds and root systems still surviving only a short distance below the scorched soil surface. Within three or four weeks it is common for new vegetation to emerge and restore the blackened soil to a verdant landscape.

New plant growth is not the only long-term effect of grassland and savanna fires. Some species of plants have wind-dispersed seeds that quickly germinate after a fire, such as fireweed, or in the case of some fire-adapted pines, have cones that open and disseminate their seeds only after a fire. Grassland fires that occur fairly early in the spring are likely to have severe effects on cool-season grasses and thus help fertilize the species that have most of their growth and seed production late in the summer. In Nebraska's prairies nearly all the important perennial grasses are warm-season grasses, whereas some of the worst invasive non-native grasses, such as smooth brome, are cool-season species. As a result, one of the few ways of controlling invasive plants, other than through chemical means, is by doing controlled burns in early spring, when cool-season species are most vulnerable to fire damage, and thereby providing space, nutrients, and sunlight for the still-dormant native plants.

The recent and increasingly effective suppression of nature-caused fires, such the one I saw as a child, has had major effects on the Great Plains landscapes. The "bald-pated" loess hills that Lewis and Clark described in their 1804 exploration of the middle Missouri Valley are no longer grass-topped, but the hills have instead been largely transformed into hardwood and red-cedar forests. And the once almost treeless prairie rivers, like the Platte and Republican, have developed narrow gallery forests of mostly eastern hardwood trees that have, like early pioneers, gradually moved westward and often merge with their western relatives in the shadows of the Rocky Mountains. Forest-dependent birds such as red-bellied woodpeckers, house wrens, and wood ducks have thus gotten "free tickets" to begin colonizing the American West, and a few western birds have similarly expanded their ranges farther to the east. It was the east-west corridor of the Platte along which hundreds of thousands of immigrants moved westward in the middle to latter-1800s, looking for new land and perhaps even gold, and it was the same route that, more than a century later, first drew me to the central Platte Valley, looking for new bird species to observe and new environmental lessons to be learned.

# PART II

*In the end, we will protect only what we love.*

—**Baba Dioum, 1968**

A different kind of prairie fire appeared in 2007, in the form of a monthly newspaper called *Prairie Fire*. Its developer and guiding light, W. Don Nelson, stated in its first issue that the mission of the newspaper would be to provide a vehicle for thoughtful discussion and civilized dialogue, in hopes of developing a message of progressive thoughts, especially on matters of social importance. Although *Prairie Fire* was launched in July 2007, Nelson had made several earlier attempts going back to the 1990s. Although the previous attempts were unsuccessful, they all ended in an agreement that the proposed newspaper should be called *Prairie Fire*. There are several metaphorical reasons for this title.

In the political context, American journalists have often reported that inspiring political speeches or fast-moving political campaigns spread like prairie fires. Examples of this use can be traced back at least to the 1840 Van Buren/Harrison presidential campaign. Don Nelson recalls reading that the same usage occurred in an historical account of William Jennings Bryan's iconic speech at the 1896 Democratic Convention in Chicago.

Additionally, prairies only thrive if periodically exposed to fire. The use of controlled burning as a habitat and land-management tool is currently in widespread use by both public and private landowners. Burning also has a twenty-thousand-year history among Native Americans, who referred to prairie fires as the Red Buffalo. Indeed, Red Buffalo served as a back-up name for the new newspaper.

Moreover, prairie fires bring renewal to the earth by allowing grasses and herbs to dominate the woody species, by killing the slower-growing shrubs and trees. Prairies are nurtured by fire; fire clears out old growth, recycles nutrients, and the deep roots of prairie plants allow them to survive both fires and drought conditions.

Thus, by using the name *Prairie Fire*, the ownership team hoped to reflect on past great and inspiring public policy ideas while at the same time promoting permanence, diversity, and resilience through thoughtful civil discourse in the present and future.

It has been my special honor to be included in many of the more than one hundred writers of the 1,080 essays that have appeared in the seven brief years since the first issue of *Prairie Fire* appeared. Volunteers disseminated the paper across what would become more than one thousand distribution sites in seven states. *Prairie Fire* was constructed with the unlikely, if not impossible, business model of preferring to distribute its copies free rather than soliciting subscriptions and relying on an informed readership to write nearly all of its articles without remuneration.

During the first seven-and-one-half years of its printed existence, a vast diversity of important issues were discussed in *Prairie Fire*. I decided to tally and break them down into broad subjective categories. In doing so, I excluded some topics such as book reviews, regular monthly columns, topical accounts of events such as speeches and art exhibits, and some nebulous or miscellaneous topics such as state politics, philosophic musings, and entertainment (only one of the nearly two thousand essays concerned football!). In descending frequency of occurrence, the most common topics covered were the following: nature appreciation and environmental interpretation (over 130 titles), water issues, conservation, health issues, agriculture and ag productivity, energy, state economics and ecotourism, local food, trees and forests, climate, immigration, applied ("green") environmentalism, environmental resources and sustainability, and prairies. Clearly, environmental issues have been matters of high concern in the minds of *Prairie Fire*'s writers. Other topics that have been visited two or more times by *Prairie Fire* writers have included ranching, farming, hiking trails, the Farm Bill, civil rights, child welfare, and college savings plans. A quick examination of almost any Nebraska newspaper will find a wildly different proportion of topics, which are heavily slanted toward (in no particular order) sports, local events, right-wing robo-head opinion pieces, and trivia.

In December 2014, *Prairie Fire* quite suddenly and unexpectedly went quiet,* at least as a printed newspaper, although its past content will be preserved in the future on the Internet. The tens of thousands of readers of *Prairie Fire* owe a huge debt of gratitude to Don Nelson, Nancy Hamer, Cris Trautner, and Aaron Vacin, who somehow managed to produce a professional-level monthly newspaper for more than seven years on a shoestring budget and a strong belief in the importance of their efforts.

Perhaps new flames will periodically re-emerge, phoenix-like, from *Prairie Fire*'s previous ashes, and like new prairie growth, *Prairie Fire* might become even better than its former self. Thinking of *Prairie Fire*'s long-term legacy, I am reminded of an ancient proverb by the Chinese philosopher Kuan Tsu, who wrote: "If you plan for one year, plant rice. If you plan for ten years, plant trees. If you plan for one hundred years, educate mankind." *Prairie Fire* has done exactly that, and in spades.

*Update: A new April 2015 issue of *Prairie Fire* appeared as this book was being prepared, and it seems that the team is back on track with the monthly newspaper.

—Paul A. Johnsgard

# Can Ecotourism Help Save the Great Plains?

Bill Taddicken, director of the Rowe Bird Sanctuary in central Nebraska, says the four saddest words in the English language are "You should have seen..." They might be followed by "vast flocks of passenger pigeons," or "oceans of rolling tallgrass prairie," or "immense herds of Buffaloe, Elk, deer, and Antelopes feeding in one common and boundless pasture." That last bit was written by Meriwether Lewis.

Taddicken's observation is double-edged. It is a lament for things not seen and that can now never be seen. But it is also an exhortation to see those natural marvels still available and to preserve them.

Taddicken's call is to see the real thing, to experience the noise and flutter of the sandhill cranes along the Platte, or smell a Sandhills prairie in spring, or thrill at the return from near-extinction of black-footed ferrets in the Conata Basin. Nature, the real thing, activates all the senses.

Today you have a growing number of excellent opportunities to see the real thing, to become an "ecotourist" in the Great Plains. But can ecotourism be more than just an interesting vacation option—can it, in fact, help save the Great Plains' remaining virgin prairie and precious biodiversity? I and other interested observers believe so, and acting on that belief, we at the Center for Great Plains Studies recently surveyed naturalists to identify the region's best spots. Mike Cooper and Linda Ratcliffe put them on the map ... literally ... our "Top 50 Ecotourism Sites" map. Our goal, beyond providing a handy guide for adventurous nature-seekers, is to aid the larger conservation effort in the Great Plains.

America's central grassland originally stretched from Illinois to the Rockies and from north Texas to mid-Manitoba, and it astonished early Euro-American travelers. Many could not get comfortable in its vastness and lack of visible landmarks, and few could resist using the "sea of grass" metaphor. Others saw the profusion of its wildlife, and it amazed them. It remained for the first true field botanists, Charles Bessey's students Roscoe Pound and Frederic Clements at the University of Nebraska, to discover the incredible biodiversity contained in each small patch of prairie, which typically harbors 150 or more different species of grasses and forbs.

As settlers remained to work the land, the prairie steadily disappeared. It was plowed under to seed fields of corn, soybeans, and wheat. Only the shortgrass prairie, beginning at roughly the one hundredth meridian and extending to the foothills of the Rockies, survives in large intact areas. But it is under terrible threat. High grain prices, improved irrigation equipment, "drought-resistant" seeds, and highly subsidized federal drought insurance (which makes row-crop farming profitable even when the plants shrivel in the fields)—all these produce incentives to plow deeper and deeper into the semiarid prairie. No one seeks to roll back settlement and cultivation, but perhaps it is time to save the grasslands that remain. Ecotourism serves as a counterweight to the plow-up.

Ecotourism provides an experience of nature both powerful for the individual and respectful of the land. Much ordinary tourism doesn't meet this standard, which is fine. But it's not ecotourism just because it happens outdoors, for example, in parks that feature swimming pools, water slides, and casinos. Many outdoor leisure activities actually harm the ecology—motorized or other activities that scar the land, contaminate the air, dim the night sky, or disrupt nature's sounds of wind and animal calls. Such entertainments do not speak to Taddicken's call. Our vision is for low-volume, high-yield tourism that creates highly memorable experiences, promotes conservation, and raises awareness of and love for the biodiversity around us. *It ought to leave the ecotourist transformed and the land unchanged.*

In defining ecotourism sites for our map, we limited locations to any place primarily devoted to environmental or biodiversity conservation that provides public access, either free or for a fee. We did not include places whose primary purpose is hunting and fishing (though ecotourist sites may permit hunting or fishing). The sites may be owned by government, a nonprofit or tribal organization, or a for-profit business. Ecotourist sites provide places to walk, hike, camp, photograph, observe, learn about, and reflect upon the wondrous natural environment that is the Great Plains; some sites also offer opportunities to engage more deeply, by volunteering or participating in programs that support and sustain this precious legacy.

So how can ecotourism help save the Great Plains? There are at least five ways:

- Ecotourism creates greater public awareness of nature and its fragility.
- Ecotourism generates revenues for parks and reserves to operate.
- Ecotourism builds public support for policies that protect the environment.
- Ecotourism gives nearby local communities an economic stake in conservation, changing them from potential opponents to benefitting partners.
- Ecotourism helps change the whole national culture in favor of conservation.

This model of ecotourism-driving-conservation is no pipe dream—it has been implemented with remarkable success in Costa Rica and the southern African countries of Namibia and Botswana. Namibia is an example of conservation success on *private* lands. It has made great strides in conservation: Unlike in most of Africa, nearly all wildlife species in Namibia show stable or growing numbers, its public opinion has swung decisively in favor of conservation, and its economy has benefited from hugely growing ecotourism revenues. And its success rests largely on ecotourism revenues.

Walking the Waterberg Conservancy you can see this strategy in action. Waterberg is a private voluntary association of eleven members—ten cattle farms and the Cheetah Conservation Fund, which owns land and has some farming operations.

The members each continue to own their farms and run their livestock, hunting, and ecotourism operations separately. The conservancy jointly manages the wildlife on the combined property of all the members. For example, one joint function is carefully monitoring animal populations. CCF organizes an annual twenty-four-hour full-moon game count, using more than ninety volunteers who count game around forty-five waterholes on conservancy farms. On the basis of its monitoring, the conservancy sets sustainable quotas for huntable species; perhaps more importantly, it is able to maintain a careful inventory of the health of all its species. Waterberg now includes about 370,000 acres, providing habitat for amazing populations of kudu, warthog, leopard, eland, hartebeest, baboon, more than 240 species of birds, and many other animals.

But you don't have to go all the way to Africa to see this strategy working. The Switzer Ranch and Nature Reserve in the Nebraska Sandhills, one of our "Top Ten" sites, is run by fourth- and fifth-generation ranchers who have combined cattle ranching with a highly attractive ecotourism destination. They are perhaps best known as the place to see prairie-chickens and sharp-tailed grouse do their "booming" and "dancing" during the spring mating ritual. Their land management philosophy is "ranching to conserve, conserving to ranch." They and their neighbors in the Gracie Creek watershed are demonstrating how ranchers can profitably combine biodiversity conservation with traditional ranching. The Switzers' conservation efforts depend importantly on ecotourism revenues.

The Switzers' work has been widely watched and applauded: the Omaha *World-Herald* noted, "Disabusing visitors of the notion of Nebraska as a 'flyover' state that's flat and boring isn't difficult—once they see the [Switzer Ranch and Nature Reserve]." *Audubon Magazine* featured it in its March–April 2010 issue, and *Travel + Leisure Magazine* named the Gracie Creek project its winner of the 2009 "Global Vision Award."

In the process the Switzers are creating positive "spillover" opportunities for other local businesses and communities—for example, other ranchers have begun to offer prairie-chicken tours, several individuals have launched wildlife-guiding businesses, and a high-end restaurant, which opened recently in Burwell, benefits when birders and others stop. The Switzers' success is of growing interest to other landowners facing higher taxes and increasing economic stress. Area citizens benefit from nature by attracting others to nature.

The American Prairie Reserve in Montana, another "Top Ten" site, offers a nonprofit model for private lands conservation. APR aims to construct a 500,000-acre private reserve abutting the Charles M. Russell National Wildlife Refuge; already it has purchased (from willing sellers) or leased about 150,000 acres. In future AMR and the "Charlie Russell" together would constitute a nearly three-million-acre wildlife reserve. AMR has reintroduced bison, and its genetically pure herd now numbers more than two hundred. Its lands contain a profusion of nearly the full array of prairie wildlife, including pronghorn, burrowing owls, elk, prairie dogs, and more. APR has received considerable well-merited praise for its accomplishments, including *National Geographic* labeling it our "American Serengeti" in a beautiful film of that name.

Other private nonprofit conservation initiatives also depend on ecotourism revenues. The central Platte River complex of Rowe Sanctuary (Audubon) and The Crane Trust are crucial leaders in maintaining and improving habitat for a half-million migrating sandhill cranes (and the few remaining whooping cranes). Jane Goodall called the migration "one of the seven wonders of the natural world." Thus ecotourism is bringing new revenue streams to private (either for-profit or nonprofit) landowners, helping them pay land taxes and financing efforts to preserve and restore biodiversity.

Of our "Top 50" sites, thirty-one are federal lands and eight are state parks; and of the "Top Ten" sites, five are national lands (Badlands National Park, Charles M. Russell National Wildlife Refuge, Theodore Roosevelt National Park, Devils Tower National Monument, and Upper Missouri River Breaks National Monument) and one is a state park (Nebraska's Fort Robinson State Park). Public lands are absolutely critical to Great Plains conservation, yet they are vulnerable to many threats: from demands to open them for energy exploration to pressure for additional road building to commercial intrusions and simple underfinancing. Deb Fischer, during her recent successful US Senate campaign, even proposed selling off large chunks of federal lands, allegedly to reduce the federal deficit. Clearly there is more education work to be done.

On managing *public* lands, Botswana is a leader. Here, wildlife and indeed whole ecological systems flourish, especially in the miraculous Okavango Delta region where water literally rises out of the desert to support an incredible array of species. Ecotourism revenues spread to a thick infrastructure of private-sector services and jobs, employing approximately a third of the local labor force, who can easily see how their economic prosperity depends on protecting the precious water and wildlife.

So, too, does ecotourism shape national public opinion in these countries. For example, Botswana President Ian Khama recently declared that his government will stop issuing hunting licenses and beef up anti-poaching measures to protect the country's fauna. Although most naturalists see controlled hunting as a useful wildlife management tool, Khama was concerned that in Botswana it was linked to the killing of elephants and rhinos. He said because elephants are the main attraction for tourists, he could never allow them to be killed. The economic pressure in Botswana appears to have swung decisively in favor of conservation.

Our work to identify the Top 50 Ecotourism Sites is, at one level, simply intended to promote greater awareness of the natural grandeur that is the Great Plains. But we have a deeper aim: to mobilize efforts to conserve, sustain, and pass along to future generations this marvelous, diverse environment that we have for so long taken for granted. In preserving what remains, let's eliminate the need to say, "You should have seen..."

—Richard Edwards

---

# Mapping the Treasures

I don't think I'm taking a risk to suggest that when most people think of places to visit in order to experience the proverbial wonders of nature, Nebraska and the Great Plains don't immediately come to mind. Fair enough. Posters of Nebraska and the prairies don't typically cover the walls of travel agencies. And if your sense of natural beauty is limited to tall mountains or sunny beaches, then you'd best book a trip to Colorado or Hawai'i. Don't get me wrong. Those places have their appeal, to be sure. I visit them myself, and when I do I have a great time. I mean no disrespect. But the wonders of nature are so much more varied, complex, and subtle than what can be encompassed by such stereotypical vacation spots, and those wonders can be found literally anywhere, not least of all on the Great Plains.

Really, though, who could blame potential visitors for not being aware of the interesting natural locations and experiences available to them on the plains and prairies when so many of the locals don't know about them either. Sometimes I ask students on the first day of class to write a short account of an experience they have had with nature. And most of the time they write about a family road trip to Yellowstone or, perhaps, a visit to Grandpa's cabin on a lake in Minnesota. Rarely do they think of the natural world of their local environments, of their hometowns, as being worth consideration as "real" nature, as worth writing about. I soon discover that most of them, though they have lived their entire lives on the Great Plains, have never seen a real prairie, can't distinguish big bluestem from leadplant, and wouldn't know a bobolink if it perched on their iPhones. But it's not their fault. A combination of forces have conspired to create this situation, to encourage this limited perception. Historical land settlement patterns, agricultural policies, mass media, and our educational system are among the most prominent culprits, but I'd best not get started griping about those or I'll never stop.

The purpose of this collection, both for visitors as well as for the locals, is to change that perception, to make it clear that yes, there is indeed a lot of very interesting, scenic, at times awe-inspiring nature to be found on the Great Plains. You may have to look a little harder to find it, but it's here.

The tallgrass, mixed-grass, and shortgrass prairies of the North American Great Plains constitute a series of distinctive ecosystems formed primarily by fire, aridity, glaciers, and the grazing action of millions of bison. While far too much of these grasslands have been destroyed, much remains. Outstanding prairie remnants survive and have been protected. If you know where to go, you can still find stunning displays of wildflowers throughout the blooming seasons. And, in an exciting turn of events, many landowners, governmental agencies, and nonprofit organizations are engaging in inspirational prairie restoration efforts, bringing leadplant, liatris, milkweed, little bluestem, switchgrass, and hundreds of other species of plants, as well as a host of interdependent insects and other animals, back to their rightful home on the prairie.

Here, too, can be found some of the best birding in the world. Birds of the East and birds of the West overlap. I speak from well-earned experience when I say that the abundance and diversity can be confusing to the casual birder. The Central Flyway brings tens of millions of avian visitors every spring and fall. And truly there's no denying the drama of the spring migration of the sandhill cranes. Jane Goodall, who's seen some wildlife in her days, calls this migration one of the world's great wildlife spectacles. Another migration, though less obvious, may be even more amazing, the annual journey of monarch butterflies southward across the Great Plains to the mountains of Mexico, only to return again the following spring.

These and many other topics are featured in this volume. The articles were all originally printed in the monthly journal *Prairie Fire*. Since it was published in Lincoln and circulated in Nebraska, most of the articles focus on features of the state, but much of what they describe can be experienced throughout the Great Plains. The articles are a varied lot. Some focus on specific places, others on specific animals or plants. Some of the articles express individual experiences in nature and their authors' rambles and reflections. Some of the authors are trained scientists, among the most knowledgeable in their fields. Others are poets, photographers, educators, and citizen scientists. They are a diverse community. But these pieces are unified by a powerful engagement with and love of place, a place too often neglected, overlooked, and demeaned, and so a place truly in need of some loving.

A lot of the rhetoric surrounding the virtues of ecotourism describes the way it promotes collaborative partnerships between private landowners, businesses, various governmental agencies, and nonprofit environmental organizations. Ecotourism, so the argument goes, can promote environmental restoration as well as economic development. One needn't be entirely cynical to take this rhetoric with a grain of salt, to think, perhaps, that it all sounds too good to be true. But upon reading through this collection, you will discover that such partnerships are indeed crucial to ecotourism, that such synergies can work, and that much of the rhetoric is based not simply on hopeful idealism but on sound experience.

Whether you are a visitor from the other side of the world or a tourist in your own hometown, you will find much of interest in this collection. From hemisphere-wide migrations to the minutiae of prairie soils, the range is dazzling. If you would like to know more about the natural treasures of the prairies, this book will serve as an excellent introduction. As with a lot of treasure hunts, you may need to tramp a little and dig a little to find your jewels, but this book should serve as an excellent map by which to discover their locations.

—Tom Lynch

# PART I

## People and Places

Bison (*Bison bison*), adult male

# The Otoe and Missouria

*Four Hundred Years of History*

*By* HEATHER SARLES PAYNE

---

At one time the Otoes and Missourias, along with the Winnebago and Iowa Tribes, were part of a single tribe that lived in the Great Lakes Region of the United States. In the sixteenth century the tribes separated from each other and migrated west and south, although they still lived near each other in the lower Missouri River Valley.

The Otoes, who call themselves Jiwere (jee-WEH-ray), and the Missourias, who call themselves Nutachi (noo-TAH-chi), were related to each other in language and customs, but they were still two distinct people.

The state of Nebraska gets its name from the Otoe-Missourias. It is from two Otoe-Missouria words, "Ni Brathge" (nee BRAHTH-gay), which means "water flat." This name came from the Platte River, which flows through the state and at some places moves so slowly and calmly that it is flat.

The state of Missouri and the Missouri River are both named after the Missouria Tribe, which once lived in the region and controlled traffic and trade along the Missouri River and its tributaries. Trade was a vital part of Otoe and Missouria life for centuries. They traded with the Spanish, French, and Americans for various goods. All three nations courted the Otoes and Missourias for exclusive trading agreements.

In the summer of 1804 the Otoe and Missouria were the first tribes to hold council with Lewis and Clark in their official role as representatives of President Jefferson. The captains presented to the chiefs a document that offered peace while at the same time established the sovereignty of the United States over the tribe.

Unfortunately, contact with Europeans also brought new diseases. Smallpox decimated both tribes and weakened their hold on the region. The Missouria Tribe lost many people to disease, and warfare with other tribes killed many of the healthy warriors. In the late 1700s, with few people remaining, the Missourias went to live with their relatives the Otoes.

The Otoe-Missourias were predominately hunter-gatherers. They did grow and harvest corn, beans, and squash, but this mostly subsistence farming was intended to supplement the bison and other game that made up the majority of the Otoe-Missouria diet. As was their tradition, the tribes would migrate to follow the buffalo, but they stayed in a general area of Nebraska, Iowa, Missouri, and Kansas.

The traditional lands of the Otoe-Missouria people were desirable farming lands to the settlers from the east. As more and more settlers came onto Otoe-Missouria land, the tribal people fought to protect it. Although a small tribe, the Otoe-Missourias bravely fought any who attacked them, including the white settlers who had essentially squatted on the tribe's land. This created a conflict for the United States government, and the government took action to protect settlers. In 1855 the Otoe-Missouria people were confined by the United States government to a reservation on the Big Blue River in southeast Nebraska.

Life on the Big Blue Reservation was hard. The tribe was not allowed to hunt for buffalo. The government encouraged a shift from a migratory lifestyle to an agrarian one without consideration of long-established tradition or social structure. For years the tribe watched as acre by acre of their land was sold off by the government to non-Indians. They suffered as treaties were broken and food, medicine, livestock, and basic essentials were not delivered as promised. Sickness was rampant, children starved, and the mortality rate climbed higher year after year.

In 1881 they were moved to Red Rock, Oklahoma, where the tribe is currently located. Otoe and Missouria children were taken away from their parents and sent to government boarding schools to be "civilized." The children had to learn English. Tribal elders remember being punished for speaking their native language at school. The stigma of speaking the traditional language passed into the home. Some tribal members did not teach their children their language because they did not want them to be punished in school or because they thought it would be better for them to learn "white ways."

Because so many of the traditions and the language were discouraged by the government, much of the language has been lost. Today the tribe is struggling to maintain what knowledge of the language still exists. Some of the information gathered by the tribe regarding the language was documented by non-Indians, missionaries, and government agents.

In 1834 a missionary named Reverend Moses Merrill created a system of writing the Otoe language. He published a book of Otoe church hymns called *Wdtwhtl Wdwdklha Tva Eva Wdhonetl*. The title of the book translates to "Otoe book their song sacred." This book is considered to be the first book ever published in Nebraska.

Otoe-Missouria land was again taken from the tribe in 1887 when the US government passed the Dawes Act. The act provided for the distribution of tribally held lands in Indian Territory (now Oklahoma) into individually owned parcels. This broke up the Otoe-Missouria reservation and opened land deemed as "surplus" to settlement by non-Indians and development by railroads.

Today most of the nearly three thousand tribal members still live in the state of Oklahoma, but there are members who live throughout the United States, including New Jersey, California, Hawaii, and Alaska. The tribe is still one of the smaller tribes in Oklahoma, but led by a progressive Tribal Council, they have parlayed their gaming revenue into long-term investment in other sustainable industries, including retail ventures, loan companies, natural resource development, hospitality, entertainment, and several other projects still in development.

# Buffalo Roads and River Bottoms
*Restoring an Ancient Ecology*

*By* ROBERT KELLEY SCHNEIDERS

---

An ancient mammalian road network once crisscrossed the northern reaches of what is now the United States. Its trails had existed since the last ice age. For thousands of years large mammals—such as the wooly mammoth, saber-toothed tiger, sloth, *Bison antiquus*, and later *Bison bison*, cut pathways across the land. Over the years the mammal trails became deeper and wider from the incessant pounding of hooves. Even before humans arrived on the continent, bison, deer, and elk located the routes of least resistance through the landscape. After the peopling of North America, humans adopted those same roads for their own use.

The majority of the mammal trails traversed river and stream valleys. Within the Missouri basin, deep, wide roads lay along both sides of the Missouri and Yellowstone rivers. Smaller roads tore up the valleys of the Big Sioux, James, and Niobrara rivers. Still smaller traces trekked up creek beds such as Perry Creek (at modern-day Sioux City, Iowa), Bazille Creek and Ponca Creek (in today's northeast Nebraska), and Okoboji Creek (in present-day central South Dakota).

By the time of the Lewis and Clark Expedition the road network had become well established and extensive. Sergeant Patrick Gass of the expedition, who took on the duties and responsibilities of the deceased Sergeant Charles Floyd in August 1804, recounted the presence of bison roads in the prairie region. He remarked, "There are ... roads and paths made by the buffaloe [sic] and other animals; some of the buffaloe [sic] roads are at least ten feet wide." John Bradbury, who floated up the Missouri on a keelboat in 1811, noted the presence of a bison route near the mouth of the Niobrara River. He stated, "we observed excellent roads made by the buffaloes. These roads, I had frequent opportunities ... [of] examining, and am of the opinion that no engineer could have laid them out more judiciously." Edward Harris, the companion of John James Audubon on their 1843 Missouri River journey, remarked, "You would be surprised to see how the whole country here is trodden up by the feet of the Buffalo, and we see their deeply worn paths in all directions, they are now shedding their coats which they leave on every bush." Bison roads did not cut across the land in a haphazard, indiscernible pattern. Rather, the roads went in specific directions, connecting the region's oases with one another.

Biological diversity was not dispersed evenly throughout the Missouri Valley, the prairie region, or the northern plains. Instead, flora and fauna concentrated in what nineteenth-century European-American chroniclers referred to as "bottoms." The wide *bottomlands* that stretched all the way across the Missouri's valley floor were not the same as *bottoms*.

Bottomlands lay in the lowlands next to the river. Because the bottomlands were subject to annual inundation, the habitat there changed frequently. It could morph from a timber tract to a sand flat in one season. Bottomlands might contain a variety of habitat types, including wetlands, sand dunes, oxbow lakes, or acre upon acre of tall big bluestem grass. On the other hand, the bottoms possessed certain characteristics that distinguished them from the bottomlands.

Bottoms sat on top of the second or third terrace above the Missouri or its tributaries. Consequently, bottoms remained immune to the river's annual floods. Distance from the rising waters of the Missouri meant that the habitat types within bottoms became more stable over time. Trees had time to take root and grow, so bottoms included healthy stands of ash, oak, and hickory. Rich soils existed in the bottoms—the result of the decomposition of organic matter, the defecating of bison, and the infrequent deposition of Missouri River silt. Such soils fostered the growth of tall prairie grasses, chokecherry bushes, and mulberry trees. The wealth of edible vegetation in turn attracted bears, whitetail deer, elk, and bison, which led to the continued fertilization of the soil.

The majority of bottoms existed just downstream from the mouths of the Missouri's tributaries. A long, bountiful bottom once reached from today's Blair, Nebraska, to Homer, Nebraska. Frontiersmen knew this stretch of land as "The 60-Mile Bottom." A small bottom existed between the mouth of Perry Creek and the mouth of the Floyd River (where today's Sioux City now stands). Cottonwood trees grew on the fringes of those two waterways, while the flat in between the streams grew wild flowers and big bluestem. Another bottom could be found east of the mouth of the Big Sioux River beneath towering loess hills. Because the land within this bottom rarely sank under the flooding Missouri or Big Sioux rivers, it held thick, old oak trees at the time of European-American settlement.

On the south side of the mouth of the Vermillion River, in present-day southeast South Dakota, could be found another bottom. In 1833 Prince Maximilian of Wied remarked on this ecological sanctuary. He wrote, "We continued our voyage, but soon lay to at the prairie, on the right bank, because Mr. McKenzie wished to form a plantation at this place. The whole plain [or bottom] was covered with high, dry grass. On the bank of the river there was a fine border of tall timber trees, in which the turtle-dove cooed... At the spot where we now were, it is said that large herds of buffaloes are seen in the winter."

Along the south bank of the James River where it joined the Missouri, a bottom with lofty groves of cottonwood trees spread out. Another bottom blanketed the Missouri Valley just below the mouth of the Niobrara (where the town of Niobrara, Nebraska, once stood). Prince Wilhelm, a member of the German royalty, viewed the Niobrara bottom in 1823. He recalled, "The southern bank near the mouth of the [Niobrara] stream expands into a beautiful prairie region with tall grass." The valley contained additional bottoms further north.

The bottoms represented oases or pockets of fertility in an occasionally stingy land. When drought struck the semiarid grassland of the northern Plains and shrank the available forage, bison, deer, and elk trekked into the bottoms to find fodder. During cold and snow-filled winters, those same animals found shelter in the bottoms among the trees and high grass. Bottoms enabled the valley's creatures to survive during inclement weather and periods of extended drought or cold. During the era of European-American agricultural settlement, farmers occupied the bottoms—converting habitat to cropland. The bottoms also became disconnected from one another as roads, fences, towns, and farms disrupted animal migratory routes.

Since the 1990s, the Army Corps of Engineers, in cooperation with the US Fish and Wildlife Service and state conservation agencies, has been working to restore the Missouri River ecosystem. Much of the rehabilitation effort has involved the reopening of the Missouri's former side channels, the re-creation of sandbar habitat, and the formation of wetlands adjacent to the big river. In the wake of the 2011 flood, that restoration work has come under fire from Missouri Valley farmers and their congressional representatives. But the critics of ecosystem recovery need to understand that river restoration contributes to flood control. The widening out of the Missouri's channel area, the reconnecting of the main channel to side channels, and the creation of wetland habitat in the valley bottomlands will diminish future flood heights and decrease the velocity of floodwaters—which will lessen damage to agricultural land in the valley. The reestablishment of riparian habitat will provide numerous ecological, economic, and social benefits.

But it should be noted that the recovery of the Missouri River ecosystem requires more than opening former side channels or re-creating widely separated wetlands. A healthy, self-sustaining ecosystem will necessitate the reestablishment of some of the former bottoms as oases. Those refuges will then need to be coupled to the ancient mammalian road network. If this is not done, and restored habitat remains isolated in small, disconnected patches, ecosystem restoration will be slowed or stopped altogether. Without continuous stretches of habitat and the ability to move freely between regions, species will continue to suffer higher incidences of predation and human interference—which will increase species mortality rates. We need to think of Missouri River recovery on a larger, regional scale.

# A Place Called Pahaku

*By* Paul A. Johnsgard

---

There is an area in eastern Nebraska where the Platte River, after flowing northeastwardly from the vicinity of Kearney for nearly 150 miles, enters the glacial drift bordering the Missouri Valley and turns directly east. Over its eastward course of about fifty miles, the river forms a shallow and wide sandy channel that is bounded to the south by forested bluffs and to the north by a wide, wooded floodplain. One of these glacially shaped and loess-capped bluffs was known historically to the resident Pawnee tribe as Pahaku (usually but incorrectly spelled as Pahuk) Hill. This Pawnee word may be roughly translated as "mound on or over water" or "headland." The bluff is one of five natural sites (four of them along the Platte River) in the historic range of the Pawnees that were considered sacred to them, and it is the only remaining location that is still virtually biologically intact. About fifty thousand years ago, during late post-glacial times, this bluff also marked the approximate point where the

Platte River abruptly turned southeast. It then followed a glacial moraine valley, now known as the Todd Valley, toward present-day Ashland. Although this part of the lower Platte Valley is now recognized for its uncommonly rich bottomland soils, it is also rich in Pawnee history, since the Platte and Loup valleys were among the most important parts of the Pawnee's original homeland.

Pahaku Hill is located almost directly north of Cedar Bluffs, in northern Saunders County. According to one Pawnee legend, a young boy once lay at the edge of the bluff hoping to shoot a bird with his bow and arrows. Growing at the edge of the bluff was a tall cedar tree marking the entrance to a huge cave that was the lodge of many animals. Several eagles and a hawk sat on the cedar tree, perhaps serving as guardians. A second underwater entrance to the cave also existed, which could only be reached by following a kingfisher as a guide. The chief of the animals living in the lodge was a giant beaver, but the lodge also was the home of other spiritually important animals, such as deer, elk, antelope, wolves, coyotes, foxes, cranes, and geese.

These were known to be sacred animals (*Nahu'ac*) by the Pawnee, and in this cave they periodically held council. There they also endowed the young Pawnee boy with special healing powers, which he later passed on to others of his village. At times such medicine men visited Pahaku to renew their healing abilities and to give thanks. Of all the Pawnee animals having spiritual powers, birds were especially important. They served as direct messengers to the gods and played significant roles in important Pawnee ceremonies. Eagles were the most preeminent and powerful of these totemic birds, and hawks were also notable, as were their feathers. Owls were particularly significant in Pawnee healing ceremonies, while other species such as jays, magpies, and woodpeckers were appreciated for their own valuable attributes. For example, the intelligent magpie helped the legendary Pawnee child find the entrance to the Pahaku cave. There probably once was an actual cave at this site, as several of the Pawnee's sacred sites along rivers consisted of bluffs with caves, but erosion no doubt destroyed it long ago.

In a different and perhaps more authentic version of the legend, after a young boy had been sacrificed by his father and placed in the Platte River, two turkey vultures delivered his body to the sacred animals in the cave. The sacred animals brought him back to life and taught him all of their medicine powers. He later went back to his people to serve as a great medicine man and transmit his knowledge.

The Pawnee's peaceful bison-hunting and agricultural culture was eventually destroyed by the impact of European immigration, partly as a result of the destruction of their bison-dependent economy. Their vast homeland, which once stretched from the Niobrara to the Arkansas and Cimarron Rivers and numbered about twenty thousand people by 1820, was decimated by smallpox during devastating plagues in 1831 and 1832. Adding to this catastrophe, part of their land was sold at a pitifully small price to the US in 1833. Later losses of ancestral Pawnee territory were associated with the Kansas-Nebraska Act of 1854 and the ceding of tribal lands for settlement by immigrants. The Pawnees were soon limited to a small reservation along the Loup River, now Nebraska's Nance County. Eventually even this tiny remnant of their homeland was lost to settlement pressures. In

1874 the last of the Pawnees (about two thousand) left Nebraska, when all the adults walked to a small reservation in Indian Territory, now Oklahoma. At this time they were under periodic danger from attack by the Lakotas and were being increasingly surrounded by white settlements. After their reservation school year was over, the Pawnee children were similarly moved to Indian Territory. According to Pawnee oral history, they, too, walked the entire distance; after their shoes and moccasins had worn out, they had to walk barefoot, with some dying along the way. The Pawnee reservation now consists of about twenty thousand acres, and the population near the end of the twentieth century consisted of about 2,400 Native Americans, or about one-tenth of the estimated presettlement number.

Pahaku was homesteaded in 1868, and it was not until the forested part of the bluff was purchased by Dr. Louis and Geraldine Gilbert in 1962 that any attention was given to preserving its natural habitats. After learning of the location's great spiritual significance, the Gilberts applied to have the site placed on the National Registry of Historic Places, which was approved in 1973. During the 1980s, their land was preserved for posterity through a conservation easement. More recently the Gilbert's land was sold to Kirby and Mary Zickafoose, who are equally determined to keep it in a natural and protected state. The remainder of the bluff has been farmed by the Pat and Nancy Shanahan family for more than a century, and in September 2008 a delegation of Pawnees visited Pahaku to help celebrate the establishment of a conservation easement on the Shanahan's 257-acre farm that will protect that part of the bluff from further development.

Because of Pahaku's history and transitional location, linking the eastern deciduous forest plants and the prairie riverine forests, "Ty" Harrison, a University of Nebraska-Lincoln botanist, did an ecological analysis of the site's plants in 1984. He found that several eastern deciduous forest trees (bitternut hickory, black walnut, and American linden) approach or reach the western edge of their Platte Valley distribution at Pahaku. There are also several eastern woodland vines (carrion flower, bristly greenbrier, eastern virgin's bower, and Virginia-creeper) and many woodland wildflowers (jack-in-the-pulpit, columbine, pale touch-me-not, white snakeweed, and American bellflower) that have similar eastern forest affiliations and range limits. Farther to the west, the drier climate and absence of a shaded forest understory increasingly prevents these plants from thriving and reproducing. In these ways Pahaku represents a kind of botanical eastern outpost, which also supports a comparable array of eastern forest-adapted animals such as eastern fox squirrels and white-tailed deer.

On a cold morning in mid-April 2010 I drove to Pahaku with a friend, to meet with its long-time caretaker and fierce protector, Cherrie Beam-Clarke. Cherrie also has served for three decades as an interpreter of the land's natural and Pawnee history and is an educational speaker for the Nebraska Humanities Council. The wild plums were then in full bloom along woodland edges, while the leaves of most of the forest trees were just unfolding. Newly arrived migrants from the tropics, such as brown thrashers and eastern phoebes, were establishing territories, while permanent residents, such as red-bellied and downy woodpeckers, were making their presence known with territorial drumming. We walked a trail to one of the higher points on Pahaku Bluff, an open area of prairie where the carcass of a whitetailed deer had provided food for wintering bald eagles. From the hill we could visualize the course of the old Pawnee Trail that paralleled the southern bank of the Platte River, leading to distant Morse Bluff on the western horizon.

Walking along the bluff's steep slope, we flushed a pair of wood ducks from the trees where they had no doubt been looking for a suitable nesting cavity. Wood ducks are another eastern species that, like red-bellied woodpeckers, has progressively moved west along the Platte Valley woodlands. In addition to the widespread and early-blooming blue violet, we found a few examples of Dutchman's-breeches. This delicate eastern woodland flower is very near the western edge of its Nebraska range, and at Pahaku it is limited to the bluff's steep and shady north-facing slopes, where it often grows among mosses and ferns. Its pinkish flowers resemble baggy upside-down pants hanging from a clothesline, through the narrow "waist" of which bumblebees must pass so they can reach the pollen tucked away in its spurs. The other early spring wildflowers we most wanted to see, the columbine and jack-in-the-pulpit, had not made their brief but beautiful appearance. Like many other deciduous forest plants, they have evolved adaptations allowing them to bloom and be pollinated before most sunlight is cut off by the leafy summer canopy.

We did find another botanical goal: the oldest bur oak in the area, which no doubt was already an impressive tree when the Pawnees were still living peacefully along the Platte. The great oak is still producing a few acorns but is slowly dying; one of its largest lower branches had recently broken off and lay desolate on the ground. The tree's twisted shape reminded me of an ancient Pawnee holy man, lifting his arms in anguish toward the sky and lamenting the fate of his dispossessed people, who now live in a reservation over five hundred miles away from their homeland.

## References

Bristow, D. "Pahaku—Nebraska's Center of the World," *Nebraska Life*, November/December 2005, 31-36.

Clarke, C. B. "Pahaku and Pawnee History" (an unpublished collection of materials related to Pahaku in the Nebraska State Historic Society, Lincoln, Nebraska), 2009.

Cunningham, D. "Pahuk Place," *Nebraskaland*, June 1985, 27-31.

Grinnell, G. B. *Pawnee Hero Stories and Folklore: With Notes on the Origin, Customs and Character of the Pawnee People* (Lincoln, Nebraska: University of Nebraska Press, 1861).

Harrison, A. T. "Pahuk Bluff Historic Natural Area. A Report on the Natural History, Ecology and Anthropological Values, with a Biological Inventory Survey, Master Plan and Management Recommendations" (typescript report, photocopy in Nebraska State Historic Society library, Lincoln, Nebraska), 1984.

Sands, D. "People, Partnerships and Preservation: A Landscape of Opportunity in the Lower Platte Valley," *Prairie Fire*, March 2009, 12-15.

Weltfish, G. *The Lost Universe: Pawnee Life and Culture.* (Lincoln, Nebraska: University of Nebraska Press, 1977).

Wishart, D. *An Unspeakable Sadness: The Dispossession of the Nebraska Indians.* (Lincoln, Nebraska: University of Nebraska Press, 1994).

# Hinterlands

*By* MICHAEL FARRELL

―――――――――

## Smiley Canyon Overlook

It is Friday, May 23, 2008— Memorial Day weekend. I'm sitting in my car, which is packed with photo gear, in a steady drizzle parked at an overlook near Fort Robinson, Nebraska. My cell phone says "No Service." I'm writing on scrap paper unearthed in the car. The laptop is back at the Hilltop Motel in Crawford, which has no Internet service, let alone wireless connectivity.

I'm out of touch. And that's a good part of the reason I'm here.

Even though the primary focus of this trip "out west" this weekend is to make photographs and I'm dead in the water waiting for the weather to lift, I'm a happy man. As Dwight Yoakum sings, "I'm a thousand miles from nowhere. Time don't matter to me. 'Cause I'm a thousand miles from nowhere and there's no place I wanna be..."

The photographs displayed here are all from places characterized by very low population density, stark but striking landscape, relative inaccessibility, and not much conventional or commercial tourism appeal. These are parts of Nebraska, Wyoming, and Colorado where you can spend an entire day on backcountry roads or trails and not see another person.

These places, even though they appear rugged or harsh, are also fragile environments that may not survive, as we experience them now, too far into the future. The effects of climate change, the demands for new energy development, or other dramatic forces may alter them in major ways, both in terms of their appearances, but also in their ability to sustain diverse communities of plants, animals, or people.

Many of the photographs in this collection are from places I've visited over and over for many years. Many embody a particular "genius loci," or spirit of place which has the power to challenge, jolt one out of familiar patterns of thinking, and which can help heal the soul frazzled and frayed by the incessant demands of a frantic media environment in unrelenting fast forward.

I go to these places to stop and take a look. Full stop—long look.


## Nebraska

Whenever I head west to photograph I try to stop at Ole's in Paxton for a buffalo burger and then on to an overnight at Ogallala. The next morning it is up early for the short drive north

*Crow Butte and Little Crow Butte with storm clouds*

across Kingsley Dam and on out just past Lewellen to the first
right turn that follows the Blue Water upstream into the Sandhills. That's where the trip really begins.

This first stretch was where the Sioux under Little Thunder
were camped in September of 1855 when General Harney's men
fell upon them at first light in retaliation for the Grattan Massa-
cre near Fort Laramie a year before. Crazy Horse was a youngster
in one of the villages and witnessed the destruction of many of
his people that morning.

The Blue Water flows out of Crescent Lake in the heart of the
Sandhills. It's easy to imagine why a horse-based culture would

value this avenue through the dry country. It is a beautiful way to get where I'm going, and it usually takes the better part of that first day to get rid of the tensions and start to see anew.

By early afternoon the Pine Ridge is in sight and we're almost there.

The Oglala National Grasslands in Sioux and Dawes counties, Nebraska, is characterized by gumbo roads and two-track trails across the vast prairie, abrupt eroded bluffs and stark sculpted landforms, and the occasional lone cottonwood. And it is mostly dry, too dry for the six or more years I've been coming here to photograph—a sensitive landscape perched on the dry divide between the Sandhills and the Black Hills.

In 1877 Crazy Horse and his people passed through here on their way in from the Powder River country to surrender at Fort Robinson. Less than a year later he was dead and one way of life passed with him. A generation later, after many of the early homesteading and ranching families started going belly up in the '20s and '30s, the government stepped in and bought them out, converting this area to leased grazing land managed under the US Forest Service.

This is the far corner of the state, mostly suited to short-grass ranching, although even that can be dodgy. A big problem is finding young people willing to live in relative isolation to carry on the ranching way of life into the twenty-first century now that they've experienced the Internet.

In recent years proposals have been put forth to try to increase ecotourism, turn a few cowboys into guides, provide a new source of jobs for the youngsters, and increase revenue for ranchers and townsfolk alike. All of this would depend on

*Twin Mounds, Oglala National Grasslands*

changing traditional ranching practices to allow species like prairie dogs and bison to share land with range cattle and thereby create a more "eco-friendly" experience for visitors. If you un-build it, they will come...

In the six or so years that I've been visiting this area to photograph (usually for a week at a time), I've only seen or talked to four local people, a small group of university researchers, and one pair of tourists while out on the grasslands. It is rare to see another vehicle, let alone have a conversation.

The locals were a lone grizzled rancher on an ATV who wanted to know if I was lost and a ranch couple who saw me photographing their pond and Angus from the dirt road and wanted to have a look at my camera. The other guy was also a rancher, but works as a contractor to manage the pastureland for the Forest Service. He was fixing a gate I needed to drive through.

The pair of tourists were two guys in their late forties from Pennsylvania who come out every spring to hunt prairie dogs, both on the grasslands and on private ranch property. As they said, "We get to shoot at deer or elk once or twice in a hunting trip, but here we can shoot at prairie dogs three hundred times a day!"

These random encounters say a lot about the isolation of the place and about the way it is perceived both by people who live there and those who might be drawn to visit.

While the ranch folks I met were friendly enough, it is very apparent that the casual tourist is not welcome to wander onto private land—for photos or otherwise. Given well-meaning but cow-ignorant tourists, tricky barbed-wire gates, tight fences, and the likelihood of getting the family sedan very stuck in sand or mud, this is totally understandable—but still not very welcoming.

Most of the time I've spent there, I've been all alone. Typically I get up at dawn and go out with a location in mind for the morning. I find myself thinking about all the great American landscape photographers who went west in the nineteenth century to bring out photographs of places that later were designated national parks or valued wilderness lands.

My hero is Carleton Watkins, who packed a glass-plate camera that made 20 × 22-inch negatives that had to be coated with a liquid collodion/silver nitrate emulsion in the field and then

*The Boar's Tusk, Sweetwater County, Wyoming, E.O.D.*

exposed and processed on the spot before drying out! He made some of the first pictures in Yosemite in the 1860s. And his work helped convince Abraham Lincoln to set aside the place in trust for the public, a first step in creating today's national park system.

I think of my work as a part of that same tradition: taking the time and trouble to get to an area well off the beaten path and to find the iconic images that characterize my visual experience to bring back and share with people who probably won't go there themselves but whose curiosity or sense of "belonging" may be aroused by seeing the images. And it doesn't hurt to have a few stories to go with the pictures.

My day usually begins at dawn when the light for landscape is good for a few hours and doesn't end till an hour or so before sunset. I use lots of maps and usually have a few places in mind as I start the day, but it almost never goes the way I imagine. Wind, clouds, rain, even hail can change what or where I try to photograph. So the day usually is an improvisation with driving, hiking, and eating lunch out of the cooler on the car hood.

In this part of Nebraska I've been in a severe hailstorm that caused three thousand dollars in dents to my vehicle, been backed up slowly by an angry bull, come as close as I'd ever want to stepping on a rattler, realized that my adrenal glands work just fine, and gotten comfortable with the idea of talking to myself when under extreme stress.

But that's a big part of why I do this. It sure isn't because there is any money in it.

I have used four different cameras for this body of work. Most of the images in this collection were done with a Swiss-made Sinar monorail view camera that makes 5 × 7-inch traditional film negatives. The majority of the panoramics were made with a 4 × 5-inch Sinar and a few with the 5 × 7-inch. In the past year I added an 8 × 10-inch back for the bigger Sinar, and then I bought a special 8 × 10-inch field camera that can be backpacked to places I can't carry the very heavy Sinar.

I have a collection of ten large-format lenses with focal lengths varying between 65 mm to 400 mm. I develop my own film and make my enlargements in a darkroom that I built decades ago. My enlarger only handles negatives up to 5 × 7-inch, so recently I bought a scanner and digital printer to make large prints from the 8 × 10-inch negs.

Each of these pictures takes a long time to set up and shoot. The camera has to be assembled on a big tripod. Composition is on a ground glass the same size as the negative where I see the image upside down and reversed left to right. I have to choose a lens, make a composition, decide on filters, take light readings, and then when everything is ready, load the film into the back of the camera, wait for the calm moment or passing cloud so I can trip the shutter for an exposure that lasts anywhere from a quarter of a second to fifteen seconds or more. Ten or fifteen set ups between sunup and sundown is a very productive day.

It is very easy to make mistakes, and you don't get to see the results until the film comes out of the chemistry in the dark-room weeks later. This isn't instant gratification.

Spend a few days out alone in this landscape and it is easy to come a bit unglued in time. Once when I was photograph-ing an anthill and waiting for the wind to die down, I was pac-ing around near my camera. I noticed a pile of broken rock and stone. I was on a high point overlooking a valley. Some of the flakes of stone had sharp edges and looked to me to have been worked. (An archaeologist friend later verified this.) It was easy to imagine Paleolithic hunters sitting here waiting for game to come to the stream below— working chunks of stone into points and scrapers.

From where I was standing it was only a couple of miles across the valley to the bluff called Round Top. Below that hill along a creek bottom is Hudson-Meng Bison Kill where ancient people trapped, killed, and butchered hundreds of bison as long as ten thousand years ago. Now, very near that same spot, here I was, a middle-aged Irish-American guy with a big camera waiting for the wind so I could take an image of an anthill...

## Wyoming — Rocks, Sand, and Canyons

My Wyoming is characterized by the kind of places that must have inspired Hanna-Barbera when they created the background art for "The Flintstones." Most of my explorations have been in the North Platte Valley and on west up the Sweetwater—the path of the old Oregon Trail (about which I made a PBS documentary that originally aired in 1997). Recently I've branched out a bit farther afield looking for similar landscapes.

The North Platte in Wyoming is well suited to big dams and reservoirs. The river has cut deep canyons and gorges along much of its path throughout the southeastern quadrant of the state. And the same geologic uplift and erosive forces have made for interesting formations and natural rock monuments throughout the region.

Beginning in far western Nebraska with the well-known attractions like Chimney Rock and Courthouse and Jail Rocks and on west into Wyoming past places with names like Devil's Backbone or The Boar's Tusk, from well before the time of the fur trappers and overland emigrants who wrote about them, these places have aroused our natural human curiosity and sense of wonder and have made for tall tales, storytelling, and myth.

I'm drawn to these monoliths and canyons because they stand in contrast to the landscape that I call home but more so because of the connection they provide to a version of "America" that preexists the name. Here the bones of the continent show through. These are places that have gone by other names, have been seen by peoples whose ways of perceiving the world is vastly different than ours is today. And these rocky places have seen species come and go before there were any conscious beings present to remark on their passing.

Now the area is home to a new wave of energy exploration and exploitation. Natural gas and coal-bed methane extraction are expected to increase in many areas of Wyoming, putting pressure on today's sensitive habitats and species.

Like the other places depicted in this exhibition, for most of us much of the North Platte drainage in southeastern Wyoming is out of sight and out of mind. Beginning in the late nineteenth century we've altered parts of this landscape to irrigate croplands downstream and to generate electricity. When I first started going there to see the big dams, reservoirs, and canyons, I only saw people at the Bureau of Reclamation campgrounds boating or fishing on the weekends. I could drive my car right up to the dams and have free and solitary rein to photograph.

Today that has changed with increased fear of terrorist attack on major infrastructure sites. Signs warn the public to stay away. I've been stopped a few times by armed security guards who appear from nowhere in response to my attempts to photograph. They must have their own cameras and video surveillance devices.

I suppose a guy with a big black box on his back and tube-like device in a bag over his shoulder walking across a dam that holds back a couple of million acre-feet of water could be up to no good.

But I'm actually just a wandering Nebraska photographer interested in the light on these ancient American rocks at this particular time of day, in this mid-summer season of this young and unsettling century.

## Back at the Smiley Canyon Overlook

Now it is the end of the day. Although the sun broke through in the afternoon, the wind never let up, pounding in from the south at forty miles an hour. No photographs today—and now the wind has shifted abruptly and another big dark front is racing in from the west.

We're headed east fast, away from what looks to be major hail, on Sugarloaf Road past several of my favorite places, small spots with no names but totally characteristic of the Oglala National Grasslands, when a group of three antelope doe spook up and start racing the car. They get up to thirty-five miles per hour and cut across the road in front of us. Up ahead we see the big buck. This is their place. Always has been.

Around the bend is a little seasonal wetland with avocets and yellowlegs wading. I've never noticed it wet here before. Maybe it is greener this year?

Dwight Yoakum sings, "I'm a thousand miles from nowhere..."

# Secrets of the Most Sincerely Dead
## *Agate Fossil Beds National Monument*

*By* PAUL A. JOHNSGARD

---

Agate Fossil Beds, in Sioux County of Nebraska's northwestern panhandle, is situated among heavily eroded shortgrass plains and ancient bluffs, where the still-tiny Niobrara River cuts a meandering thin blue line through an otherwise arid landscape.

Agate's fossil beds are about twenty-two to twenty-three million years old, in strata deposited during early Miocene times. North America's western plains were then undergoing a gradually drying climate, with the Rocky Mountains still rising to the west. As the growing mountains increasingly intercepted the moisture from the Pacific Coast, the climate of the plains to the east was slowly changing from rich temperate forests of the early Oligocene to a drier, more savanna-like vegetation in the early Miocene.

In the Agate region, a proto-Niobrara River was then a well-developed river, bringing in sand and silt sediments from the nascent Rocky Mountains. Seasonally dry winds deposited volcanic ash over the river sediments of the adjacent valley, forming a layer of materials that would later be known geologically as the Harrison Formation.

At some point, a prolonged drought descended on the region, drying up the wetlands and reducing the river to no more than a trickle. Water-dependent mammals and other animals died in the thousands if not tens of thousands, many where they had taken refuge in the last surviving waterholes. During the drought, their remains were buried in sediments filling dried ponds, waterholes, and abandoned stream channels. The bones of a few species of mammals, such as rhinos, accumulated in huge random aggregations extending over a large area within the Harrison Formation. Later sediments overlying the Harrison Formation at Agate (the Anderson Ranch and Running Water Formations) also show evidence of severe and prolonged drought, during which countless additional skeletal remains accumulated and gradually fossilized.

The myriad of fossilized animals that have been found at Agate are mostly comprised of the remains of more than six hundred examples of a tiny rhino (*Menoceras*) with small, paired horns near its nose, but there are also many gazelle-like camels (*Stenomylus*), and some predators. One of the predators (*Daphaenodon*) slightly resembled a whippet and is called a beardog but is not related to either the dog or bear group. Excavators found the bones of a small oreodont (*Merychyus*) in the beardog dens, a probable major prey species.

In addition to these variably recognizable mammalian types, there were examples of several strange mammals now long extinct. One of the common mammals (*Dinohyus*) resembled a giant pig and was a member of a large group of generalized omnivores called entelodonts. *Dinohyus* was as large as a bull, had powerful cloven hooves, massive jaws, and was perhaps the most formidable predator of the time. There were also nearly twenty examples of a horse-sized and sloth-like herbivore (*Moropus*) belonging to a long-extinct family of browsers called chalicotheres that had died together at a waterhole during the drought. *Moropus* had long forelimbs tipped with three long claw-like hooves and short, strong hind limbs. It probably walked in a slanting, hyena-like posture and may have stood erect, using its claws to strip vegetation from trees.

Other mammals common in the fossil array were members of a once widespread North American group called oreodonts, which were mostly rather sheep-like and even-toed ungulate herbivores with short legs and rounded faces. Among the most remarkable mammals found were a few examples of an antelope (*Syndyoceras*) that superficially resembled modern pronghorns. Like pronghorns, it had a pair of bone-based horns near its ears but also had another branching, Y-shaped horn located just behind its nose. There was also a primitive beaver (*Paleocastor*) that dug strange corkscrew-shaped upland burrows in colonies, rather than building aquatic lodges in the manner of modern beavers. The helical shape of the burrows, like a spiral staircase, may have made vertical climbing easier.

Over millions of years, this great bone bed became covered by several hundred feet of sands and silts dropped by streams and carried in by winds, eventually burying the bones but preserving the skeletons with little distortions. Later erosion cut away and reshaped the landscape, carving out two large hills where harder caprock prevented the softer, fossil-rich sediments below from being carried away downstream. These two adjacent buttes are known, west to east, as Carnegie and University Hills, which together contain the major fossil beds and arguably represent the two most famous and scientifically valuable hills in the state of Nebraska.

The human history of the area is a saga of cowboys, Indians, and bitter professional competition for fossil specimens among some famous paleontologists. Not long after Captain James Cook moved into western Nebraska, he married and acquired a large ranch about twenty miles south of Harrison, which he later named the 04 Ranch at Agate Springs. Captain Cook (his "Captain" title was honorary, although Cook served for a time as a Cavalry scout) also became friends with some of the Lakota branch of the great Dakota ("Sioux") nation, who were increasingly being restricted to the newly established Pine Ridge Indian Reservation about one hundred miles to the northeast.

One of Cook's strongest friendships was with Red Cloud, the famous Lakota chief who, in return for Cook's many kindnesses toward the recently defeated and homeland-bereft Lakotas, gave him such gifts as one of his own shirts, several pipe bags, and a whetstone owned by Crazy Horse. Several hundred of the items Cook gathered from the 1880s through the early 1900s can be seen at the monument's visitor center.

Cook was fond of collecting rocks and other artifacts from his ranch. He shipped one of his prize finds, a fossil leg bone that he had picked up in 1885, to Professor Edwin Barbour, third director of the Nebraska State Museum. Cook encouraged Barbour to visit the Agate area in 1892, marking the start of a long series of investigations by scientists from the University of Nebraska. Representatives of several major eastern museums, such as the Carnegie Museum in Pittsburgh and Yale's Peabody Museum of Natural History, soon followed.

James Cook met O. C. Marsh, chief paleontologist of the US Geological Survey, at Fort Robinson in 1875, and is said to have told Red Cloud that Marsh was seeking only "stone bones," and not gold, on Lakota lands. When Marsh died at sixty-eight he left much of his massive fossil collection to Yale's Peabody Museum of Natural History, although eighty tons of it remained at the Smithsonian Institution. Marsh described eighty new dinosaur species, and his chief paleontological rival, Edwin D. Cope of the Academy of Natural Sciences in Philadelphia, named fifty-six. Only thirty-two of their collective total are still recognized as representing previously undescribed species, but these collections consisted of what Charles Darwin once described as "the best support for evolution." They also helped spark an enormous public interest in dinosaurs that continues unabated today.

No dinosaur bones have been found at Agate, and only a very few have surfaced elsewhere in Nebraska, since most of Nebraska was inundated by a shallow sea during much of the Mesozoic era. The last dinosaurs became extinct more than forty million years before the Agate beds were laid down, and the only large Mesozoic vertebrates so far found in the state have been large aquatic reptiles such as plesiosaurs and turtles.

About fifty miles to the northeast of Agate is a less famous site of much younger deposits (about ten thousand years old): the Hudson Meng Bison Bone Bed near Crawford. There, the remains of up to six hundred bison can be seen at a very early Native American kill site. The bison were of a species transitional between the modern bison and a prior directly ancestral species, *Bison antiquus*. Together with Nebraska's Agate and Ashfall fossil beds, the Hudson Meng site provides visitors with a stunning portrait of mammalian evolution in North America, spanning more than twenty million years.

The University of Nebraska State Museum in Morrill Hall (UNL city campus) features a remarkable selection of fossil animals from Agate, including assembled skeletons of *Dinohyus*, *Meropus*, *Menoceras*, *Syndyoceras*, and the oreodont *Merychocoerus*. There are also two spiral-shaped casts of burrows made by *Paleocastor* and a preserved section of the Agate waterhole floor that is rich in bones of *Menoceras*. Behind the fossils is a huge mural depicting Carnegie and University hills. This painting was done by the Nebraska artist Elizabeth Dolan, whose evocative images may also be found elsewhere in the museum.

Agate Fossil Beds National Monument is located about twenty miles south of Harrison, Nebraska, off Highway 29. When a friend and I last drove that stretch in late May, we counted over 130 male lark buntings perched or performing beautiful flightsongs over the adjacent shortgrass prairies, as well as western meadowlarks, upland sandpipers, and long-billed curlews. The fossil beds are within an area of about 2,700 protected acres of scrub grassland and were named a national monument in 1997. Walking paths take one across a wooden bridge over the diminutive Niobrara River to the major excavation sites. The visitor center has reconstructed *Moropus*, *Dinohyus*, and *Daphaenodon* skeletons, and Captain Cook's extensive collection of Native American artifacts.

# References

Bouc, K. (Coordinator). "The Cellars of Time: Paleontology and Archeology in Nebraska." *Nebraska History* 75(1):1–162, 1994.

Cook, J. H. *Fifty Years on the Old Frontier.* Norman, OK: Univ. of Oklahoma Press, 1980.

Maher, H. D., G. F. Engelmann, and R. D. Shuster. *Roadside Geology of Nebraska.* Missoula, MT: Mountain Press, 2003.

National Park Service. *Agate Fossil Beds National Monument.* Washington, DC: US Department of the Interior, 1980, 95 pp.

Plate, R. *The Dinosaur Hunters: Othniel C. Marsh and Edward D. Cope.* New York, NY: McKay Co., 1964.

# Saving the Pawnee Mother Corn

*By* DEB ECHO-HAWK AND RONNIE O'BRIEN

We live in the Cornhusker State, but do we know just how deep the history of corn is in Nebraska? We see a lot of cornfields and we know our economy is greatly impacted by it, but how much do we really know about the first corn that grew here? Did the pioneers bring it with them?

It may surprise a lot of people that corn was a well-developed crop in Nebraska long before any European pioneers came here to settle.

Let's go back hundreds of years ago, back to a time when rivers and streams wound their way across the tallgrass prairie. The only roads were winding paths used to follow the buffalo. Some of Nebraska's first inhabitants lived in large, rural communities in circular lodges made from the earth—reminiscent of the legend of the beaver house—earthlodges. Others lived in circular tipis, following the buffalo wherever they went, having no stationary homes. Beyond the settlements of those who lived in earthlodges were fields of beans, squash, pumpkins, and watermelon, but mostly fields of corn.

For the Pawnee Nation, which called a good portion of Nebraska and Kansas home for over six hundred years, women grew the crops. They planted large cornfields, being sure to keep each variety apart from the others to avoid cross-pollination. They planted the seed in round hills, with the hills a man's footstep apart from each other in no particular direction. Hundreds of acres were planted to feed the tribe, which was once larger than ten thousand people but dwindled from diseases to three thousand by 1870.

Like buffalo, corn was a staple food of the Pawnee. And like the buffalo, it was sacred. An ear of corn and a buffalo skull were known to adorn the sacred altar in each earthlodge. Corn was an important part of every Pawnee ceremony and every feast and was eaten at almost every meal during the year. It was never, ever traded because it was so sacred.

Like other farming tribes, the Pawnee grew their own varieties of nonhybrid corn that they developed over hundreds of years. Each variety was pure in color. In other words, it was nothing like the Indian corn that we think of today, with multicolored kernels. They grew Red Corn, White Corn, Blue Corn, and Eagle Corn, to name a few. The women would walk up to eight miles in one direction with their buffalo-shoulder hoes in order to work all of their corn a second time before leaving in June on the summer buffalo hunt. Then the corn was on its own, with the tribe returning in September for the harvest. Massive amounts of corn were stored in underground caches to be used for the coming year.

In the mid-1870s the United States government forced the Pawnee to move to Oklahoma, and they took what corn they could carry in each family's sacred bundle on the long walk. The Pawnee were not allowed to hunt buffalo before leaving. Many of them died on the way to Indian Country in Oklahoma, leaving less than one thousand in the tribe, and their corn failed to grow year after year in the new land.

Four generations later the seeds were few and on the verge of extinction.

In the 1980s a Pawnee family living in Colorado, the Echo-Hawks, returned to the traditional practice of farming by hilling corn, as it was done by their ancestors. This practice was the one that was carried over in 1997, when the seeds were then returned to Oklahoma.

Numerous projects of the Pawnee community are aimed at the revival of tribal culture and the education of Pawnee youth. Since 1997, the Pawnee community has recognized the importance of finding the Pawnee seeds.

In the spring of 1998 a call from the Culture Committee for traditional seeds went out to the tribal members. Those who wanted to start their gardens were encouraged to bring their seeds to the reserve for elder Lula Nora Tilden Pratt to offer a blessing over. Nora was born in 1909 in Pawnee, Oklahoma, and her Indian name, *Che-Sha-Nou-Ka-Nout*, means "Are you a princess." Nora was called upon for her cultural insight. At this time the Pawnee had identified three varieties of corn: Blue, Yellow, and Eagle Corn. Nora's prayer, the blessing over the seeds, marked the beginning of the Seed Preservation Project. Elder members have participated in cultivating Pawnee traditional seeds for the Seed Preservation Project, and youth have been part of that effort on a small scale. Eventually, the nine traditional varieties of Pawnee corn were found, but not all would germinate, and some varieties consisted of only a handful of seed.

By 2003 the corn varieties had been collected, sorted, and kept under the watchful eye of the Pawnee Culture Committee and Deb Echo-Hawk, Keeper of the Seeds. In that same year the Great Platte River Road Archway in Kearney decided to begin a new school program about the Pawnee, being in the heart of the traditional Pawnee homeland. Ronnie O'Brien, director of cultural education at the Archway, contacted the Pawnee Nation, looking for help with the new program that would focus on their way of life on the Plains, including growing a Pawnee corn garden. She was referred to Deb Echo-Hawk. To the Pawnee this brought up the question of trusting someone other than a tribal member with the seeds. The Pawnee Nation Cultural Committee deliberated this question and granted their blessing to trust gardeners rather than taking the risk of losing more seeds.

The two ladies began a long-distance communication and arranged for the seeds to return home to Nebraska to grow again in the soil where they once thrived ... to begin a relationship between the Pawnee and the Archway, with the Pawnee entrusting what few seeds they had from two varieties to a few select Archway growers.

One of the first varieties of Pawnee corn to be planted by the Nebraska growers was Eagle Corn, which was so rare that Deb Echo-Hawk would keep the last remaining twenty-five kernels in 2005 in case the other twenty-five sent to Nebraska would not grow, as the first attempt in Nebraska had failed in 2004. Since then, the project has reaped many benefits.

In November 2010 the gardeners from Nebraska were invited to Pawnee, Oklahoma, for a ceremony called the Young Dog Dance. During the ceremony, Eagle Corn soup, made from Eagle Corn grown at the Archway's garden, was served for the first time in 125 years. Pawnee Spotted-Like-a-Horse beans were also served for the first time in living memory.

A new and happy chapter in history has begun for the Pawnee, one where their sacred corn has been returned to its homeland of Nebraska to be grown and then returned to the people. The Archway has since advanced the Pawnee Seed Preservation Project of Nebraska to include more than ten varieties of corn, plus beans, squash, pumpkins, sunflowers, and watermelons.

Perhaps the best news of all is that the Pawnee in Oklahoma, despite the drought and heat of 2011, have successfully grown three varieties of their own corn in the town of Pawnee, where they live today.

They never gave up hope, and they found a way to revive their corn varieties after many decades of struggle. The Pawnee Seed Preservation Project is the result of the families in Oklahoma who never gave up the cause of returning their sacred corn to their tribe.

It is amazing to see where the seeds have led us.

The seed project has led to other developments at the Archway. In 2009 the Archway helped 155 tribal members of the Pawnee Nation return to Kearney for a homecoming celebration and powwow, the first Dancers of the Plains event. In 2010 builders from the Pawnee tribe and their Arikara relatives from the Mandan, Hidatsa, and Arikara Nation of North Dakota built a large earthlodge next to the archway's Pawnee corn garden.

And there is now a profound friendship between the Pawnee, the Archway, and the Nebraska growers.

The ongoing story of the Pawnee challenge to return their nonhybrid corn for the welfare of their people is promising. Our history, culture, and traditions are important to all of us, and especially for the traditionalists of the Pawnee community. We all will pass our culture, history, and traditions to our children— that is sustainability! We want our children to feel proud of who they are, and this legacy, we feel, is priceless. In the very heart of Pawnee traditions and the present-day Nebraskan traditions, there are stories of our corn ... stories that need to be told.

# Saving Species, Saving Ourselves

*By* JOEL SARTORE

---

*This essay originally appeared in conjunction with the exhibit "Fragile Nature" at the University of Nebraska State Museum.*

Preserving endangered species saves all of us in the long run. We've heard it all many times... more people are alive today than ever before. Especially in developing nations, human over-population has reached epic proportions. All these new people spread out. All consume resources.

Though we'd hoped these problems would stay overseas, it's already started here in the United States. Especially now in the American West, this manifests itself in people fighting over water, land use, space, ways of life.

As the battles continue, many conservationists are working harder than ever to save the last of our wilderness on behalf of grizzly bears, gray wolves, and other charismatic animals. But here where I live, it's the littlest things that count the most. Case in point: the Salt Creek tiger beetle.

Found nowhere else on Earth, this is an insect that lives in just a couple of salt marshes on the north edge of my town, Lincoln, Nebraska. If I can get folks to stop and think about this for a minute, maybe the big picture will fall into place as well. I hope so, anyway.

Here in Lincoln, we have just three places that have any semblance of nature. We've got a small patch of virgin prairie out by our airport, some woodlands surrounded by housing developments and highways, and a couple of salt marshes. The marshes are the ones in the news these days because they are home to the beetle, now down to fewer than 250 adults each summer. And even though it has been federally listed under the Endangered Species Act, the developers keep coming, building housing and commercial sites in the last watershed this insect calls home.

The ESA is a whole story in itself. It's a law designed to save species, the only one of its kind in the world. Some say the law goes too far; others, not far enough. The truth is usually somewhere in the middle. All I know for sure is that we're quickly running out of wild spaces, wilderness. And we need healthy, functioning wild lands and their accompanying ecosystems to survive. So in that sense, our fate is up to all of us.

So really, why should we care about this bug and the last of our saline wetlands here in Nebraska? Why care about any endangered species? In the end, it all boils down to a few simple questions. Do we respect nature? Do we show benevolence to all life forms? Is there room for "us and them"? You decide. But you'd better hurry. Time's almost up for one species in Lincoln. The rest of us can't be far behind.

If you still need more reasons to care about a little bug and the marsh it lives in...

(1)  **Save species and habitat to help save ourselves.** To think that humans are not tied in tightly to the natural world is pure folly. In fact, we're totally dependent on healthy, functioning ecosystems for our very survival, from the air we breathe to the food we eat to the water we drink. Notice that the frogs and bird species are thinning out where you live? These things are living monitors of the health of the earth. To think that we can escape their fate over the long haul is not realistic, to say the least.

(2)  **We're killing off the ark.** All plants and animals, even the Salt Creek tiger beetle, are God's creatures. Who are we to purposely kill off any of these creations? The Salt Creek tiger beetle is our local example of the massive wave of extinction now going on around the globe, all due to human activity and overpopulation.

(3)  **Save it for education.** Ever go on a field trip to a pond or a marsh in grade school or high school? Remember the thrill at seeing the wildlife there, from frogs and tadpoles to dragonflies to the teeming life found in a single drop of water when viewed under a microscope?

(4)  **It's about more than just a beetle.** Saving the saline wetlands (or any ecosystem) benefits thousands of other animals, such as migrating ducks, geese, and shorebirds that use such critical habitat at various times of the year.

(5) **Small things lead to bigger ones.** If people care enough to save something as seemingly trivial as a salt marsh and as tiny as a beetle, then they'll surely care about the environmentally big things, like the destruction of "The Lungs of the World," the Amazon rainforest. Cutting down rainforests leads to global warming. They'll also think more about sustainable living, such as the kinds and amounts of chemicals they use on their lawns and pour down their drains, and the kinds of cars they drive.

(6) **As the famous biologist Aldo Leopold once noted, it is the last word in ignorance when a person asks about a species "What good is it?"** We are not smart enough as a species to understand what parts are worth saving and what are not. Remember the story about a good tinker not throwing away parts until he fully understands what each does? We're not even close to knowing how everything works, whether it's the prairies, rainforest, oceans, the Arctic, or even the last of the salt marshes in northern Lancaster County, Nebraska.

(7) **Let's save endangered species simply because we care.** The beetle is just one small part of the picture. The big issue is whether or not all of us care enough to preserve what we have left. Do we want to save species and habitats or do we want to simply pave over and sterilize as much as we can in the name of economics? We are a wealthy nation. If we can't do it, nobody can.

If you truly care about the environment, the last islands of natural habitat remaining are all precious, whether it's a salt marsh, a virgin prairie, or a century-old cottonwood tree. To good stewards of the Earth, all are equally worth saving.

# PART II

## Grasslands and Savannas

Prairie fringed orchid (*Plantanithera praeclara*)
and white-lined sphinx (*Hyles lineata*)

# Spring Creek Prairie

*By* MITCH PAINE

---

The booming voices of chorus frogs, the piercing melodies of red-winged blackbirds, and the soft colors of early spring hail the arrival of the new season. Walking the endless paths through the tallgrass, one can easily get lost in the expansive depths of Spring Creek Prairie Audubon Center. Many photographers, such as Joel Sartore and Michael Forsberg, have made the Prairie the subject of unforgettable moments. These moments, etched in our minds, highlight the dedication of Spring Creek Prairie to education and conservation.

The Prairie began with the acquisition of land from former landowner Kathy O'Brian. It also began with a vision: a vision on the part of Audubon Nebraska. After O'Brian expressed interest in ensuring the land be preserved as a tallgrass prairie, Audubon Nebraska purchased the land with a promise: "The mission of Spring Creek Prairie Audubon Center is to foster the understanding, appreciation, and conservation of Nebraska's tallgrass prairie ecosystems by engaging people in the site's natural and cultural resources."

Soon after its creation, the Prairie began to live up to this pledge. School groups began to filter through the prairie land, taking in the sights, sounds, and smells of the natural Nebraska tallgrass prairie. Also, shortly after the Spring Creek Prairie inception, the Land Management Advisory Committee was created, dedicated to "the understanding and conservation of Nebraska's tallgrass prairie ecosystems," states Arnold Mendenhall, the habitat manager of the prairie. "The Land Management Advisory Committee is focused on managing the prairie by researching and improving diversity of the area."

The group implemented a two-year inventory of the plant species that exist on Spring Creek Prairie, calculating the number at over 350 species of grasses, wildflowers, shrubs, wetland plants, and trees. The Land Management Advisory Committee took the lead in restoring eighty-two acres of previous cropland into wetlands to harbor an even larger diversity of animals and plants on the prairie.

In 2003 Audubon Nebraska began writing criteria for creating Important Bird Areas in Nebraska. The Important Bird Area program is an international program to highlight the conservation of birds. Kevin Poague, the project coordinator for the Important Bird Area Program, nominated Spring Creek Prairie based on its ability to support the following:

- Species of high conservation concern in Nebraska;
- Significant concentration of birds;

- Assemblages of birds associated with rare or representative habitat types;
- Restricted-range species or birds that are not widely distributed;
- Sites important to education and research.

Spring Creek Prairie was among the first of these Important Bird Areas. Each IBA must monitor the sites on which the birds reside as well as work with landowners to ensure the protection of the birds. The second part of the mission of IBAs is to educate the public and landowners about the importance of preserving the natural habitat of birds.

Spring Creek Prairie has exemplified the promised efforts to the fullest extent. Initially, the land purchased numbered at 610 acres but grew to 640 acres with the acquisition of the Wachiska Woods, a 30-acre area of trees along a creek bordering the initial prairie land. With a purchase in 2006 of 168 acres, and subsequent smaller acquisitions, the total land preserved by the Spring Creek Prairie comes to 850 acres of tallgrass prairie, as well as wetlands and riparian area.

However, Spring Creek Prairie has taken further steps to spread the message of conservation and the ideas of the Important Bird Areas. The team of dedicated staff at the prairie have reached out to surrounding landowners to create a three-thousand-acre tallgrass prairie complex, the bare minimum area to support a healthy prairie ecosystem.

Each of the participating landowners has signed a contract that states he or she will not sell the land to developers and also will encourage talks with the Prairie. The central part of this tallgrass prairie complex is the relationship between the land-owners and Spring Creek Prairie. Both sides have input on the conservation and preservation of the prairie ecosystem.

Arnold Mendenhall frequently engages in one-to-one talks with the property owners about the prairie that foster a learning process for both sides. The same situation is echoed in Spring Creek Prairie's commitment to initiating conversation with the community of Denton.

Spring Creek Prairie is also devoted to education. Clearly evident in the creation of a new, green Education Center, the education component of the Prairie's mission statement can be found in countless other examples. Initially, the visitor's center for the Prairie was the ranch house of the former owner. As school groups began to travel to the Prairie it became apparent that a new building was needed. In a gracious move, Spring Creek Prairie held off the creation of its Education Center in order to allow the allocation of funds to a sister IBA, the Rowe Sanctuary, to build its own education center.

In 2004 Spring Creek Prairie Education Center began construction. The opening of the Education Center brought a special event to the Prairie in September of 2006. Deb Hauswald, the education specialist, says, "the Education Center created a destination for people visiting the Prairie." The center provided office space for more efficient organization, exhibit space for information about the prairie ecosystem, and a space for school groups in case of inclement weather.

The creation and design of the Education Center again highlights the mission of Spring Creek Prairie. Hauswald said that the building's design included everyone's opinions, regardless of expertise. "Decisions were made with a great deal of thought," says Hauswald. After a year of discussion with architects and a year-and-a-half of construction, the building opened with an expansive, green design.

The building roof's overhang angle blocks summer rays, while collecting winter rays for maximum energy efficiency. Propane usage has decreased as the visitor's center moved from the ranch house to the Education Center, even though the square footage increased immensely.

The walls and roof are insulated with two hundred bales of biomass, harvested sustainably from Spring Creek Prairie, and four hundred bales of agricultural waste materials (wheat straw). Much of the materials used in construction was recycled, salvaged, or reused. The metal for the roof components was taken from a pipe shed, and recycled steel was used in wall studs. The ceramic tiles used in the dragonfly mosaic were reclaimed from various sources. Thousands of recycled milk jugs were incorporated in the creation of the picnic tables, benches, directional kiosk, bicycle rack, and outdoor waste receptacles.

Dedicated to educating children and adults alike, the Education Center, along with numerous tours, highlights the important points of the prairie ecosystems. As school groups make use of the prairie, Hauswald and others keep the programs student-directed in order to foster problem-solving techniques and to better the well-being of all visitors.

"We want to get kids outside," says Hauswald, "to help them to be comfortable with being outdoors." The place-based education about prairies provides visiting students the chance to develop skills rather than to simply improve a pool of facts.

A 2005 study by the American Institutes for Research showed that students involved in outdoor education programs raised science scores 27 percent and showed a higher retention rate of knowledge. Being outdoors can teach students not only science but also all other disciplines. The growing movement for peace-oriented education can also benefit through outdoor education. The 2005 study showed significant improvements in students' ability to mediate conflict and to cooperate with other students.

The objectives of the Spring Creek Prairie's commitments to place-based education include exploration of animals and habitats of the prairie. Students are encouraged to get dirty in the muddy wetland areas, to venture on the prairie trails, and to investigate the wooded areas. The Prairie Explorers program provides students the opportunity to make individual discoveries about the prairie and the natural history of the area. The Prairie Waterworks program plunges students into the world of wetlands on Nebraska plains, allowing the students to explore the habitats of wetland plants and animals.

In each of these examples, the idea of place-based learning takes precedence, involving students in hands-on activities in which the students make individual findings about the natural ecosystem of southeast Nebraska. The programs also meet a number of Lincoln Public Schools science requirements.

Many groups visit the prairie, from Boy Scouts to fourth graders. The place is also home to many festivals and events. Most notably, the annual Twilight on the Tallgrass event takes place in early September.

As students, parents, and other visitors venture out onto the prairie, the place-based education about the natural ecosystems of Nebraska can open the door to wondrous encounters. Deb Hauswald recounts witnessing interactions between a doe and a bobcat.

She glanced out the window during a typical day's work and saw a doe coming out of a ravine. The doe was very agitated, and suddenly a bobcat arose from the grass and approached the doe. After making false starts and attempting to lead the bobcat away from her position, the doe charged the aggressor. The cat curled up on the ground and began pawing at the attacking doe, which pawed back with razor-sharp hooves. Eventually, the bobcat rose and scurried away from the scene, followed closely by the angry mother deer. All the while, the shocked staff looked on as this event unfolded.

Many other examples of this tremendous display of nature can be seen. Trumpeter swans make use of the prairie, baby turtles hatch and swarm the wetlands, monarch butterflys make the prairie home during migration, as does the majestic bald eagle on occasion.

All of these examples of the spontaneity and beauty of nature can be seen, but "it's up to us to stop and take a look," says Hauswald. The prairie is a place of hidden beauty, and the beauty sometimes lies in such hidden places as the diversity of insects living down in the grass. Hauswald says, "The prairie is such an amazing place, and I am not articulate enough to express in words the wonder of the prairie."

# Prairie: Up Close and Personal

*By* Twyla M. Hansen

---

*Prairie* is from the French, a word defined as a treeless, grass-covered plain. But I would add *and so much more.* Prairie provides us with a solid sense of place, as in this is our natural heritage. Try to imagine the entire central US and Canada covered in grasses and forbs—millions of acres—alive with animals great and small, above and below ground. Prairie is the epitome of *rootedness,* as in *we are not going elsewhere,* as in *we're adapted to harsh winters, fierce winds, and punishing summers.* And in spite of losing most of this historic vegetation to the plow, we still have excellent examples of tallgrass prairie close by to experience up close and personal.

> *There is mystery here, in the shapes of grass,*
> *in the dim movements of an inland sea,*
> *connections to an earlier time.*

**Spring Creek Prairie**—just minutes southwest of Lincoln near Denton—is perhaps my favorite place on earth. To think: It was preserved by luck—never plowed—by folks who raised cattle and horses on native pasture. I can only imagine the lucky kids who once played and rode on its hills, waded in its ponds, hid in the tree-filled gullies, and marveled at its natural springs, same as other rural children. And lucky for us that the National Audubon Society recognized this place of biodiversity and now operates Spring Creek as a prairie preserve and education center on some eight-hundred-plus acres. The visiting students are lucky, too—grade school to college to adult—because of the opportunity for excellent hands-on experience in an unspoiled place. Families can check out prairie discovery backpacks to enhance their experience on its trails and wetlands. A prairie immersion program through the Lincoln Public Schools will bring 1,300 lucky fourth-graders to the prairie each fall; just imagine. The green-constructed education building and Spring Creek's knowledgeable, dedicated staff enhance prairie interpretation. But the vistas from inside soon beckon, inviting you outdoors to experience the prairie and walk on its historic wagon ruts. Fall is the prime season to visit the prairie, when the warm-season vegetation turns into a sea of golds, reds, purples, and tans, temperatures mellowing into cooler evenings. A well-kept secret of prairie is that it changes throughout the year. At Spring Creek, I have tromped through snow with friends on New Year's Day, witnessed migrating birds in spring, and marveled at meteor showers on a summer night. Spring Creek Prairie boasts about 360 species of plants, 214 species of birds, a host of mammals and aquatic creatures, and untold species of insects. When you walk, explore, or simply sit on the prairie, the air is alive with wind and buzz and birdsong. Its effluvium is the essence of Earth: Your breathing deepens and your senses heighten. There are endless opportunities here for creativity, for relaxation and restoration. The prairie invites you to discovery in every season.

*Often we are strangers to Earth, stumbling over the thorns*
*of our days. Here, sky sets fire to the silk sleeves*
*of its clouds.*

Prairies are highly adapted to harsh weather and fire, with roots extending as deep as fifteen feet in a complex ecosystem—once ranging from the Rocky Mountains to east of the Mississippi River, and from Saskatchewan to Texas—in distinct plant communities: shortgrass, midgrass, and tallgrass. Spring Creek Prairie is part of the eastern tallgrass region, dominated by grasses such as big bluestem, Indiangrass, and switchgrass. Only about 1 percent of the historic tallgrass prairie area remains, making it one of the most endangered ecosystems in the world. The key to its survival is because the majority of its biomass is below ground; just imagine. To stand on prairie is to connect with a living ecosystem that has evolved through the millennia. This vast area once supported a diverse array of plants as well as creatures, and its dense, fibrous root system formed some of the richest farm soils in the world; in fact, we owe the region's wealth to its soils. In my undergraduate soils class at the University of Nebraska-Lincoln, Dr. Sorensen once said, "We're treating our soil like dirt!" Even though I was raised on a farm, it took some time for these words to sink in. In 150 years of farming, half of our topsoil has been lost; that is an article for another time. In the meantime, thank prairie soils each time you eat local food.

*Below ground is where all can happen,*
*anchor and breakdown and bedrock, processes*
*of gritty explosion and darkened decay, the consonant*
*of winter and the blessing of rain.*

My first prairie experience was in the early 1980s with a small group led by Wachiska Audubon prairie advocate Ernie Rousek on a tour of Nine Mile Prairie northwest of Lincoln. Ernie recognized the irreplaceable value of this 230-acre tract—studied in the 1920s by University of Nebraska ecologist John E. Weaver and his students—and worked to preserve it for the future. Ernie and the Wachiska Audubon Society continue to preserve prairie remnants in southeast Nebraska today. To think, Nine Mile Prairie was preserved by accident thanks to the federal government: The land served as a buffer for World War II bomb storage bunkers near the Municipal Airport. Even to a farm gal, my first connection to prairie—land that had *never* been plowed—had a profound effect on my sensibilities and my sense of place, all shaped by connection to the land. I grew up in rural northeast Nebraska on land that had been farmed by my grandparents, at a time before widespread use of synthetic chemicals and pesticides. But expanses of native tallgrass were not part of my early surroundings. My grandparents had heard of opportunities from relatives and emigrated from Denmark in the late 1800s. They were successful on a few hundred acres of rich soil around the turn of the twentieth century. My father said his mother was often lonely here, longing for the familiar wooded hills and family of the homeland. This strange, treeless area inspired writers like Ole Rolvaag and Willa Cather, who by luck and circumstance found themselves on the prairie. The prairie that remains still inspires writers and artists today.

*Sun, wind, rain, drought, fire. Travel this*
*frayed land where tall grass rules, learn*
*the buckle of deep time. Flora and fauna,*
*sky and soil: let them blaze the mind.*

Walking, sitting, observing the experience of prairie involves the senses. Luckily, there are no neon or blinking signs anywhere proclaiming "PRAIRIE! TURN HERE!" with circles and arrows. Simply go to the prairie anytime and breathe it all in. Even when I am not physically on the prairie, I can close my eyes and picture its hills, grasses, wildflowers, birds, turtles, and insects. I can imagine the sun flaming down, shadows deepening, birds scattering before nightfall. Night brings out hiding mammals, moths, and the stars. Prairie is calming and renewing, worthy of study and contemplation, and allows us to connect with the land. Artists, naturalists, and even scientists are often lucky to find connections that lead to discoveries. The secret is to nurture that luck by paying attention. In a hurried world, we must actually take time, even schedule time, in order to nurture creativity. William Stafford, former US Poet Laureate, once said that a poem is a special kind of paying attention to language. Chicago poet Gwendolyn Brooks once said that poetry is life distilled. And I would add: Prairie is all of these, *and so much more.*

*Let the wheel of your singular mind unwind,*
*Imprint your body with each phase of the moon.*
*Be open to the unexpected, expect to be amazed.*

*Poem excerpts are from* Prairie Suite: A Celebration *by Twyla Hansen and Paul Johnsgard, 2006, Spring Creek Prairie Audubon Center.*

*Prairie facts are from the* Encyclopedia of the Great Plains, *2004, editor David Wishart, University of Nebraska Press.*

# Clouds and Concretions

*By* WILLIAM BEACHLY

---

*An essay written during the Prairie Writers Workshop, May 2010, at the Willa Cather Memorial Prairie near Red Cloud, Nebraska.*

Where are the hard edges when we consider this prairie before us? Perhaps a photograph would create the illusion of them: freezing a crystalline moment. But in motion, in real time, there are no real edges. Like Heisenberg's particles—position and place and motion are not a unity. The edges of the prairie itself as a named formation are vague too. Its very name denoting "a little meadow" shows the lack of a suitable term. Those French trappers had known no such place to relate it to. Prairie is to place as impressionism is to art: it's a genre of place.

Prairie skies are the most frenetic creatures, and truly their color and form depends entirely on externals: the angle of light rays, the dust, the nebulous ice crystals and vapors. A lone jet trail is so out of place, but it will soon be smudged and rendered part of the pastel skyscape. There go the people, I thought, that once rode the rails through Red Cloud. From that arteriole, cultures diffused into the prairie tissues of Webster County. The Swiss, the Bohemians, the Volga Germans, the Scots, the Brits.

Cather was trapped here for a time but found her lymphatic channel out through the barrel of her pen. As the ink flowed, so did the essences of this diverse place, finding a channel to the general circulation and immortality. And now a few people return to this prairie.

As clouds cast their moods on the ancient landscape below, ephemeral and leaving no trace, it is the precipitation they brought that worked and shaped this land. I'm reminded of Cather's commentary on human stories. Like clouds, no two exactly alike but the patterns repeating over and over. Pushed by the winds, the great equalizer of pressures and moisture in a Sisyphean task, one wonders, "how can it ever be still in one place and not another?" Human migrations follow these same whims, but for now Red Cloud appears to be a still place. Or is that illusory as well?

Winds brought the loess here, piled in drifts and sheets over vast ancient sea floors. Now the wind would carry it off as well but for the prairie. We forget how recent the prairie is: how Loren Eiseley reminded us that flowers, and especially grasses, changed the world. Grasses use the wind as ferns had for eons, to disseminate propagules, but both pollen and seeds are new creations of high sophistication. Grasses are anything but simple. And in the soil they have set revolutionary roots. Roots that both bind and build a black, rich, living tissue. The loess itself is blond and uniform and sterile. Grass captures and imports new elements from above, the burrowers mix, the fungi share, and the bacteria compost. All is communality. Trees are like the many immigrants before and after Cather. A few find suitable but difficult purchase here, many other pass on or perish. They raid the prairie storehouse of nutrients and crowd out the natives. But they never truly adapted here, and never will until they listen to the ways of the prairie. Treasure and embrace diversity, be compliant yet steadfast, leave a better soil behind you.

Instead they brought edges; the plow, the rail, the fence line. They had to have edges or sanity sifted away as loess crept under their windowsills. Time had to be linear. Progress required a scale, however arbitrary. What struck Cather when she first saw her childhood home here? The edges and angles of it. Europeans brought edges and hardness to the prairie, the natives preferred rounded dwellings. Their earth lodges covered by the prairie, in accordance to their circular cosmology and the minimum of edge.

My attention is drawn to the variety of soft, pliant forms at my feet. The edgiest of all are the sedges, straight and three-sided (again, the minimum edges for nonrounded stem). But even these cannot resist a splay of soft and intricate flowers, asymmetrically placed to one side. Around these I see extravagance of form and color: the showy vetchling, the scarlet guara, the evening primrose. Even the names evoke beauty and emotion. Ah, but there is a patch of prairie rose, and surely here there will be sharp edges. But the thorns are few, and tiny at that, more like accents for the blood-red stem than armament. The petals are softness incarnate, with rich red margins melding to white and pink taffy-like bases. Here they meet a circus of bold, butter-colored stamens like a tight cluster of flags. The olive leaflets have edges that defy linearity, like the edges of a chert arrowhead. On the underside, as adorns so many prairie plants, I find a soft pubescence. "I could comfortably lay down in this bed of *Rosa suffluta*," I thought. So I did.

My repose brought upon me an astonishing variety of life: metallic green bees, curious hoverflies, varicolored butterflies, and a few ballooning tiny spiders, as would occur on any random bit of prairie real estate. I decided that being prostrate, or merely horizontal, was the proper attitude in which to appreciate prairies. Someday I must try this with my contact lenses out, with uncorrected, near-sighted vision. We are sometimes too reliant on vision. Closing my eyes I absorb the sounds, smells, and tactile stimuli. I could hear and feel the vegetation moving, the hum of insect trespass, the melodic call of distant birds, the curious clicks of cricket frogs at some unseen distant spring. All this is merely air in motion, but rich in latent meaning. Set in motion by the collective metabolism of the prairie.

Beneath me I could imagine the burrowing and probing of Stygian life of the hypodermic layer. In mysterious, unseen ways I knew concretions were forming there. They are the closest thing to rocks in this prairie, but softer with no edges. They grow like little prairie eggs, some so large they were called by the Germans the Loess Kinder—children of the prairie.

I found one of these where a badger had excavated a gaping maw in a loess bank. It's a fitting memento of this day. I thought of their varied forms beneath me as I watched the cloud forms passing over. Each one begins around a nucleus, be it a mote of dust, a tiny, intricate land snail shell, a shrew's tooth, or a bit of bone. It grows under the influences of all around it, kind of like Cather. Stories, too, are concretions about a nuclear idea or emotion, with the same amorphous properties of similarity and uniqueness. But one difference remains. This concretion will grow no more but wear away. Stories can do likewise, but some are immortal. As for clouds: They bear watching.

# Keith County, Nebraska

*An Introduction*

*By* JOHN JANOVY JR.

---

The Cedar Point Biological Station is a University of Nebraska mini-campus located eight miles north of Ogallala, with thirty or more buildings nestled in the canyons along the south shore of Lake Keystone, below Kingsley Dam, and offering a variety of classes. I was sitting in the CPBS dining hall recently, discussing a colleague's potential field trip to Estes Park.

"There are people," I offered, "who believe that if you've seen one mountain, you've seen them all."

He stopped eating and stared at me for a few moments.

"And you're one of those people," he finally said.

I nodded; truthfully. My wife Karen and I had just returned from a couple of weeks in Alaska. I was appropriately stunned by the Alaskan scenery and took at least three thousand digital photographs. At that picture-taking rate, if we'd stayed up there another month, I might have approached my photographic total for sunrises over Lake Keystone, sunsets over Lake McConaughy, the Keystone-to-Roscoe road, and the grain elevator at Roscoe.

After thirty-five years of summer ecological research and teaching in western Nebraska, the thousands of Keith County photographs seem like an effort to capture the essence of this experience: the emotions, personal thoughts, and professional satisfaction of projects brought to closure, the reactions of students who came to CPBS having never been west of Grand Island then went home with a bad case of what we call "The Ogallala Blues," and, finally, the mysterious but lasting effects that Sandhills colors have on a person's view of the world. Along the westbound lane of I-80, a road sign between Sutherland and Paxton proclaims "Entering Keith County." That sign could just as easily be referring to your mind as to your truck.

To a biologist who studies tiny organisms, the diverse habitats of Keith County represent a highly accessible supply of problems to be tackled, problems that teach a person how to approach all kinds of challenges, how to manage resources necessary for any intellectual endeavor, and how to talk about one's work to diverse audiences. But the fun part of that experience is not restricted to professional scientists. Anyone can, and probably should, take photographs of the Sandhills at daybreak and at sunset, maybe even several thousand of them. Anyone can, and probably should, drink from a well, look closely at the mixture of natural vegetation along a gravel road north of Paxton, and spend half an hour watching dragonflies at that small pond down the hill from the Game and Parks Visitors Center. Simple as they are, these activities enrich enormously the time spent in Keith County; they are value-added freebies.

At the south end of Kingsley Dam there are turnouts from where a person can see the length of Lake McConaughy to the west or the Lake Ogallala/Lake Keystone complex below the dam to the east. Any time of a summer day there are likely to be people parked at either place, simply looking, taking pictures, capturing for their later use an image of Keith County's signature physical features, albeit ones constructed by humans. A quick check of vehicle license plates reveals a diverse population of visitors, but to a person, they've simply stopped to look. With a little luck, they'll stop somewhere else and drop a few coins, but for the moment they're doing something that is completely free: studying landscape. No mountains can be seen from either of these turnouts.

Over the years my family has dropped a few coins in Keith County, too, but what we've brought back home are the colors, the smells, and the visions. A Facebook posting of photographs inevitably brings a flurry of comments, not only from our children but also from former University of Nebraska students—all CPBS alums—now scattered around the globe. "Wish I was there" is a frequent response to storm clouds over the Sandhills. "I can still smell the wet grass" comes in response to a full rainbow. The comment "can't even see the sky from where I live now" makes me wonder why, perhaps aside from family and a job, a person would live where he or she could not see the sky.

There is no hard scientific evidence that the Sandhills landscape makes an indelible mark on a person's mind and emotions, a mark that person carries forever, but there are many reasons to believe that is the case. Foremost of these reasons is the reaction of people whose encounter with Keith County occurred years ago, but at the time involved something more than simply waterskiing on Lake McConaughy. These "Keith County Alums" spent significant time observing landscape at several scales, watching the sky and getting acquainted with people who lived in this environment the year around. Thus we have a Keith County model for how tourists can greatly enrich their travels regardless of their destinations: Look for the subtleties in landscape, study the colors, breathe in the smells, get out into the weather, talk to locals in their own establishments, and, by the way, take thousands of pictures and drop some coins.

# Prairie Diversity

*By* CHRIS HELZER

---

Some of my favorite people are insects. I also have a thing for plants. Fortunately, I spend a lot of my time hanging around in prairies where no one mocks me too much about my preferences for companionship.

When I can't be out in a prairie, one of my other favorite pastimes is talking to people (yes, real people) who haven't spent much time in prairies and introducing them to the kinds of things they're missing out on. Prairies contain an amazing array of insects, animals, and plants, most of which are easy to miss if you're not looking carefully. There's the inchworm that camouflages itself with bits of the flowers it eats, the crab spider that can change color to match the flower it hunts on, and ants that manage herds of aphids and harvest sugary sap from their rear ends. Among birds—besides the recognizable meadowlark—there are many other species, including the bobolink—which looks like a blackbird after a lobotomy and sings like

R2-D2 from *Star Wars*, the pencil-necked upland sandpiper—a shorebird that gives a wolf whistle call as it circles overhead and then perches on fence posts, and the sedge wren—whose machine gun song matches its aggressive territorial behavior toward other bigger birds. These and thousands of other insect and animal species live among plant communities that contain hundreds of plant species. You probably wouldn't recognize the names of most of those plants, but even among the more familiar names there is amazing diversity. A single prairie can hold five or more species of sunflower, eight to ten species of milkweed, and well over thirty species of grass.

Preserving biological diversity in prairies (and elsewhere) is important for the sake of the individual species, each of which has its own long history of adaptation and survival. But high species diversity is also key to the survival of the entire prairie. Diverse communities are stronger and more resilient than those that are less rich in species. More overlap in the ecological roles filled by various species means that the temporary loss or decline of one species can be compensated for by others. During periods of drought, for example, some plant species wither and die or go dormant for long periods of the hot, dry summer. But a diverse prairie will have plenty of drought-tolerant species that can quickly expand into those newly opened spaces—helping to ensure a constant food supply for herbivores and decreasing the vulnerability of the prairie to invasive species. When wetter times come again, the community resets itself, with those species best adapted to current conditions becoming more abundant accordingly.

Because of the complex interactions between species in a diverse community, the loss of one or a few species can have cascading impacts on the larger community. For example, many insect larvae feed only on particular plant species for food (and often need entirely different plant species as adults). A commonly used example in prairies is the monarch-sized regal fritillary butterfly, which feeds only on violets as a caterpillar and then relies on a variety of flower species as nectar sources when it becomes an adult. The loss of violets means the loss of the regal fritillary. The loss of too many insect species can mean a smaller and less dependable food source for predatory insects and animals, and so on.

Species that provide ecological services like pollination can be even more important. Native bees are a diverse group, but they all rely heavily on the consistent availability of pollen and nectar through the season. Most native bees are solitary—as opposed to eusocial insects such as honey bees and bumblebees—so are just single moms trying to find enough food to stay alive and to store for their larvae. Since not all bees can harvest from all types of flower, a diverse mixture of flowers is necessary at all times to provide for the entire bee community. If there is a gap in flower availability during the growing season, it can mean starvation for bees. The loss of bees, of course, can then lead to the loss of reproductive ability for many of the flowers that depend on them.

Besides the moral obligation many of us feel toward the conservation of species and natural communities, there are also self-serving reasons for humans to be concerned about biological diversity. The most obvious of those reasons may be simple aesthetics. Who wouldn't rather walk through a meadow filled with hundreds of flower species—with colorful floating butterflies and myriad singing birds—than a field filled only with brome grass? Or listen to the innumerable songs of birds, insects, and frogs on a cool summer morning in a lowland prairie instead of the relative silence in a football field's worth of bluegrass turf? But biological diversity provides other tangible benefits as well. Insect pollination is a well-recognized ecological service and, as mentioned earlier, relies heavily on a diversity of both pollinators and plants to persist. And because diverse grasslands provide higher and more stable productivity, maintaining that diversity is of critical importance for our livestock industry and the people it feeds.

## The Need for Management

Making biological diversity a primary goal for prairie management is a relatively recent phenomenon. Throughout our history, we humans have managed prairies to attract game species, and, in more recent times, to maximize forage production for domestic livestock. And for as long as humans and prairies have coexisted, countless other species have flourished in those human-influenced grasslands. In the face of fires, droughts, and massive bison herds—and also because of them—thousands of plant, insect, and animal species found suitable habitat and survived. When fire, drought, or grazing made a species' habitat less favorable in one place, that species would either move somewhere else or hunker down and wait for better conditions to return.

Today, however, widespread row-crop agriculture has left many prairie landscapes with only small, scattered patches of grassland within a matrix of cropland. As a result, prairie species are much more vulnerable to changing habitat conditions. Moving across the landscape to find better habitat is much more difficult because it entails crossing large areas of unfriendly habitat, including roads, crop fields, and woodland. Hunkering down to wait for better conditions to return is also less effective than in the old days because fire, bison, and drought no longer spin the wheel of grassland fortune. Instead, today's prairies tend to be static—easily categorized as hayed prairies, grazed prairies, or prairies left idle to be consumed by opportunistic trees. If this year's habitat conditions don't suit a particular species, those conditions are unlikely to be any different next year or for many years to come. As a result, those static habitats support a limited number of species.

In addition to the challenge of surviving in isolated, static grassland patches, today's prairie species also have to contend with a horde of invasive and aggressive species. Some of these are non-native species like smooth brome, Siberian elm, and leafy spurge, but others, like eastern red cedar and dogwood, are natives that have been released from historic shackles (e.g., fire) that had kept them suppressed. These and many other invading species can become so dominant that they displace other species, reducing the diversity of the overall plant community.

## Managing for Biological Diversity

Despite all of the complexity associated with prairies and management challenges, managing for biological diversity may boil down to one key strategy: Create a wide variety of habitat patches across a prairie and change their location over time. The result is something like a patchwork quilt that is disassembled and reassembled in a different pattern each year. Each habitat patch is differentiated by its vegetation structure, which can range from short and sparse to tall and dense, as well as mixed heights and densities in between. A "shifting mosaic" of these habitat patches accommodates the needs of many wildlife species, which can travel relatively short distances to find suitable habitat each year. Less mobile wildlife species and plants can usually survive a few years in less than ideal habitat as long as better habitat conditions return often enough. Because the conditions in any one place change over time, it's difficult for any species or group to exert excess dominance over others. This includes predators, pathogens, invasive plants, and others.

Managers can alter habitat structure by using a variety of tools, including combinations of prescribed fire, grazing, and mowing/haying. The timing of those treatments changes which plant species will recover first and how quickly they will regrow. Grazing by cattle or bison can be particularly valuable because they graze selectively, as opposed to the "all-or-nothing" defoliation by mowing and burning treatments. The timing and stocking rate of grazing treatments can greatly influence which plant species animals graze, how intensive that grazing is, and how the prairie recovers. Low-intensity selective grazing by cattle or bison can create unique and valuable habitat conditions consisting of short grass and tall wildflowers. That mixed-height vegetation allows insects and reptiles to thermoregulate easily by moving quickly between sun and shade while feeding, and also provides excellent brood-rearing habitat for birds such as quail and grouse, whose tiny chicks need overhead protection from predators but short grass to move around in.

A dynamic regime of habitat management can also favor plant diversity, which is critically important to overall prairie health. Pollinators and herbivores, for example, rely on plant diversity to provide consistent feeding options through long growing seasons and through both wet and dry years. In addition, diverse prairies have been shown to be more productive and more resistant to invasive species encroachment than prairies with low plant diversity. Creating a shifting mosaic of habitat patches should facilitate plant diversity because of the varied timing and intensity of management treatments required. However, it is still important to ensure that no plant species are perennially prevented from flowering and producing seed, at least periodically.

## The Upshot

The world has changed dramatically for prairies and people over the last century or two, and this century may bring even more dramatic change than the last. Although many prairies have been degraded and/or relegated to small isolated fragments, their continued existence is a testament to their resilience.

Prairie conservation is one of the greatest legacies of our state. We have some of the most expansive and highest-quality prairies left in the world, and Nebraskans' appreciation for prairies and the need for their conservation continues to grow. The biological diversity of prairies has helped them survive so far. With smart management and responsible public policy, we can make sure that bobolinks, crab spiders, and milkweeds continue to make Nebraska's great landscapes their home far into the future.

# Why We Need Native Wildflowers

*By* BENJAMIN VOGT

---

I'll just come out and say something to alienate lots of folks: I believe our landscapes should be planted with mostly native trees, shrubs, flowers, sedges, and grasses. And by mostly I mean 80 percent, 90 percent, 100 percent. I know, I know. But I'm the kind of guy who sees a cause and knows that to even get halfway, you have to push for all of the way. And yet folks still aren't sure what "native" means or where to find them. Nurseries often have a sparse collection; independents have more; but big box stores have practically none. All have a large number of cultivars and hybrids—not the straight species plants that can sometimes be more robust and particularly attractive to wildlife.

OK, so I believe we should have at least 50 percent straight species native plants—trees, shrubs, flowers, sedges, and grasses that, before European westward expansion, were prevalent in your town. (It's like the current food movement—most of what we eat didn't even exist one hundred years ago, and the same could be said for plants; I mean, did Lewis and Clark see Native Americans tending to their tall fescue?) I say all of this not because I have any belief that we can or should return to some presettlement perfection, because we can't; no, it's about the insects who evolved in ecosystems alongside plants, both adapted to one another from flower to leaf, both symbiotic, all the beginning and end of the food web from bee colony to human dinner table. Of course, since 2008, we've plowed up over thirty thousand square miles of remaining prairie —often marginal land that cannot sustain crops; commodity prices soar and crop insurance takes the risk out of the equation. With those prairies go native bee species, which are many times more effective at pollinating food crops than honeybees. Furthermore, 100 percent of songbirds feed their young insects, and songbird populations decline every year.

"I love monarchs," someone will tell me, eyes brightening as we both ogle a photograph. I ask them if they have milkweed. "Oh no, should I? I have lilac and butterfly bush, and see them on there." Do you have baptisia? Willow? Elm? Oak? Do you have side oats grama grass? Viburnum? Bird's foot violet? Zizia? Bluestem? If you don't, I bet you see just one-twentieth of the butterflies (and their larva) that you should, not to mention other pollinators you never knew existed. During the winter of 2012-13, the overwintering population of monarchs in Mexico dipped to its lowest level ever at just three acres, way less than the record forty-five acres nearly fifteen years ago. We spray pesticides too much—lawns use up four times as much as all agriculture in the US. We have GMO corn pollen laden with pesticides that insects carry off with them. Our lawns are barren wastelands for wildlife, druggies dependent on more juice atop zapped soils full of dead soil microbes. The CDC tested nine thousand people for twenty-three common pesticides and found the average person had thirteen in their system.

Don't buy into those big-box home improvement commercials where a crazy man in a flame-retardant suit gets out his blowtorch to attack his weeds or an exasperated young couple needs only Miracle-Gro products to make their landscape fit the suburban ideal. You can garden more cheaply and easily: Use prairie plants adapted to our clay soil and weather extremes so you won't have to rush to replace them or buy fertilizer or feel tortured anguish at your needlessly black thumb.

Gardening with natives is about giving up certain levels of ownership to your landscape. Life isn't a battle royale with nature. Gardening with natives is about sharing, about living with the world and not in it; with the world and not against it; with the world and not apart from it. Bridging the gap. It's about taking a leap of faith that you are this planet's faith given momentary form, bound to its rhythms, and when you struggle to remake or ignore those rhythms, everything seems intangibly off-kilter—we suffer higher food prices, eroding shorelines, dirty water and air, new bacteria-resistant to antibiotics.

My wife told me about a story she saw on Facebook where someone was concerned about the masses of bees at their blooming crabapple tree. Their kids often climb the tree and might get stung. Should they spray the tree, they asked? Remove it? Someone suggested a dousing of chili powder spray. Finally, someone talked about colony collapse, pesticides, habitat destruction. I have put my head into bloom after bloom for six years now, literally had bees and wasps landing an inch from my nose and ears, and have not been stung. I have, though, been transfixed, overjoyed, unburdened, and generally at peace. Come to my table, I think, come share this great purpose and hope. There's more divinity in a bumblebee pushing open a baptisia bloom and pulsing its body than there is in a hymnal or stained-glass window.

This is my plea, and a sort of pledge I want you to take with me, if you want to do something massive with minimal effort: Plant one milkweed. Tell your neighbor about milkweed and the decline of insects. Tell your child. Get them to touch caterpillars. Plant an aster, a mountain mint, a joe-pye weed, a liatris, a goldenrod. Plant one native, something that helps insects. Put the plant out front with a spotlight, maybe one of those flashing arrow signs you can rent. Have the sign read: "This is a native plant, adapted, low maintenance, of benefit to dwindling wildlife, and I'm in love with it." Feel free to change the sign's wording.

# Restoring Oak Savannas

*By* SIBYLLA BROWN

---

Landowners in south-central Iowa are setting their woodlands on fire to restore globally endangered oak savannas. Temperate-zone North American oak savannas are one of the world's most endangered ecosystems. Once stretching from Minnesota south to the Texas Hill Country, presettlement oak savannas, the transition between the eastern deciduous forests and the tallgrass prairie, encompassed thirty million acres. One of the top ten ecoregions for diversity of reptiles, birds, butterflies, and vascular plants, this two-tiered community consists of open-canopy deciduous trees over an herbaceous ground layer of grasses, sedges, and wildflowers. It contains many globally and federally endangered plant and animal species and numerous unique plant communities.

Oak savannas evolved after the retreat of the last glaciation when aboriginal Americans began using controlled burns. Fire was the Indians' primary technology. It has been well documented in books such as Omer C. Stewart's *Forgotten Fires* that they burned their lands annually, sometimes twice a year. Fire was used to drive game, facilitate hunting, renew grasses for pasturage, clear brush, and increase seed production. The open woodlands also facilitated travel.

Most of these savannas have been destroyed by clearing, plowing, or overgrazing. Now only 0.02 percent remains. Since European settlement in the early twentieth century, fire suppression has turned the unmanaged remnants into closed-canopy forests with dense understories of invasive brush and pole timber. However, unlike the many Midwest prairies that have been lost to agriculture or development and can only be reconstructed, savanna remnants can be restored. Woodlands that have not been plowed will sustain portions of their native plant diversity. All they require to release the suppressed plants is sunlight and fire.

The European settlers believed that fire would destroy their timber. Many people still associate woodland fires with the conflagrations of western US wildfires and believe that fire destroys woodlands. Just the opposite is true—fire is essential to savanna ecology. The thick bark and deep roots of oaks, the dominant savanna trees, makes them fire-resistant. Fire will only destroy what doesn't belong.

Many southern Iowa landowners agree and are restoring thousands of acres of overstocked woodlands with thinning and fire. The earliest restoration, Timberhill, in Decatur County was begun in 1993. Working with their district forester, the Timberhill landowners began their restoration by thinning the overstocked oak and hickory woodland. In 1995 they implemented annual prescribed burns to control regrowth and invasive brush. Stimulated by fire and sunlight, the Timberhill woodlands soon exhibited a dense cover of native grasses and sedges. This cover not only controlled erosion but improved soil fertility. Soon uncommon flowering plants such as white prairie clover, leadplant, and false foxgloves filled in the understory. Without any interseeding this two-hundred-acre restoration now supports over 450 vascular plants. From early spring until fall frost there is always something blooming in the Timberhill woodlands.

Some conservationists believe the best way to preserve woodlands is to put a fence around them and keep people out. That given enough time the processes of ecological succession will take over and heal the land. While they are passionate about the need to save the songbirds' winter habitats in Central and South America, they are unaware of the importance of temperate North American woodlands to songbird survival. It is here, where they were born and raised, that they return each spring to propagate their species. A constant food source is necessary for them to successfully breed and to raise their young. In savanna restorations this is provided throughout the growing season by insects feeding on the understory plants. In 2006 a study at Timberhill found the breeding bird population to be strikingly different between the managed woodlands and adjacent unmanaged land. Thirty species of birds were found to be breeding in the thinned and annually burned Timberhill plots, whereas only four species (all cavity nesters) were noted breeding in the unmanaged plots. The open woodlands are also preferred habitat of the red-headed woodpecker, whose population is seriously threatened by habitat decline.

Savanna remnants can easily be identified by the presence of "wolf" trees, the widely spreading oaks that were once the only trees in a particular site. Their lower branches will probably be dead from overcrowding and lack of sunlight, but the size and breadth of wolf trees makes them stand out even in heavily overstocked woodlands. The ground layer will usually be dominated by sedges. Savanna remnants can also be identified by studying historic documents such as the original General Land Office survey notes and USDA aerial photographs.

To restore savanna, most woodlands need only sunlight and fire. This is best achieved by a combination of understory thinning and annual prescribed fire. Annual fires are much less destructive than periodic fires. With lower fuel loads, annual fires scud over the surface of the ground, leaving much invertebrate habitat intact, whereas periodic fire incinerates, parboils, and kills because of the heavy fuel buildup. Fire alone can be used to restore oak savannas, but it takes much longer.

In southern Iowa we have learned that the best practice is to burn a restoration for three years before thinning. Fire will clear much of the invasive brush and some of the weed trees, making thinning easier. The next step is to clear any remaining brush and trees growing under the crown of the wolf trees. We have observed that savanna restoration proceeds in three stages. In stage one the understory fills in with common native forbs such as woodland sunflowers and tick trefoil. In stage two the woodland sunflower and tick trefoil gradually decline and are replaced by sedges, grasses, and moss. In stage three the common forbs disappear and conservative forbs take their place. This restoration proceeds slowly and can take ten years.

For the landowner doing restoration the most difficult task is determining the correct canopy density. Is enough sunlight reaching the understory to restore plant diversity? Interseeding of savanna indicator species is often recommended, but this may lead to unexpected consequences. An inventory of plants taken before proceeding with restoration followed by annual monitoring enables one to track progress and measure the changes in floristic quality. Listen to the plants and they will tell you when you've thinned enough. Given enough time and persistence, each site will develop its own unique character.

Since 2003 US Fish and Wildlife Service private lands biologist Gregg Pattison has been assisting southern Iowa landowners in restoring their woodlands. In addition to providing cost-share funds for thinning, he provides technical assistance, particularly for prescribed burns. He has worked with landowners to demonstrate how to conduct a prescribed burn and construct firebreaks and has helped them identify highly restorable savannas. The Fish and Wildlife Service has also sponsored the Southern Iowa Oak Savanna Alliance, an organization that provides a forum for people interested in restoring and preserving oak savannas. SIOSA sponsors fire training and restoration workshops for landowners.

In cooperation with the USFWS Iowa private lands program, three thousand acres in twelve counties are currently being restored, and six county conservation boards have set aside oak savanna demonstration plots. Woodlands have been restored in other states throughout the range of presettlement oak savannas. In her 1985 survey, "The Extent and Status of Midwest Oak Savanna," Victoria A. Nuzzo found 113 sites totaling 2,607 hectares of high-quality savanna, but ongoing restoration efforts in southern Iowa and other states proves the extent of highly restorable savannas to be much greater.

# PART III

## Forests, Rivers, and Wetlands

Wood duck (*Aix sponsa*), adult pair

# On Planting Wildly

*By* JACK PHILLIPS

---

Our discovery of a white oak grove required of us considerable wandering. They were not the trees we had been looking for; those had been mutilated by a county right-of-way edict. But our grove of fifty or so trees was safe in a savanna adjacent to a narrow farm lane that had been either spared or forgotten by the chainsaw gang. The corridor that had been so savagely cleared might have been overlooked as well, as it was remote and rarely traveled. But the possibility that one day this road would see heavy traffic outweighed the rarity of a white oak stand in the eyes of the authorities.

We had gone to a lot of trouble to find these rumored trees. This population of white oaks (*Quercus alba*) was located at the extreme western reach of its range. Though abundant in adjacent northwest Missouri, white oaks are rare in Nebraska. In former times they might have ranged farther west, but whites, along with other oaks, were heavily logged during the early days of settlement. White oak lumber was prized for sturdiness and resistance to decay, making it valuable for flooring, posts, tool handles, and other pioneer needs. It was particularly desirable for making casks. For this reason, my woodsman uncle knew it as "stave" oak.

Our search for acorns went unrewarded save for one old oak that overhung the farm lane. It was loaded with fat, ripe acorns that had not yet begun to fall. Fortunately, I was accompanied by Robert Smith, a professional seed collector who has the advantage of being part squirrel. Our only other asset was my '98 Honda. Most of the acorns were out of reach as Robert perched precariously on the canoe rack while I worked the clutch. The resulting rocking and pitching put Robert in reach of one more acorn and then another as he dangerously careened like a vertiginous squirrel on the roof of the moving car.

We didn't have to worry about traffic or the law on that lonely lane. However, my lurching and Robert's acrobatics did fascinate a far-off farmer sitting on a tractor that was even older than he was. Suspicion, consternation, or befuddlement compelled him to change vehicles and investigate. We tried to appear nonchalant as he pulled up and rolled down his window. To our delight he turned out to be a well-spoken man of generous spirit. He was a lifelong resident of that land and a devoted steward of oaks.

This man and his neighbors had largely refrained from clearing the remnant woods on their land. In addition to white oaks, other native oaks grow in that county: bur (*Q. macrocarpa*), red (*Q. rubra*), black (*Q. veluntina*), blackjack (*Q. marilandica*), and chinkapin (*Q. muhlenbergii*). His land contained beautiful specimens, and we were delighted to learn of his ethic. After giving us a local history lesson and granting free access, he drove off in his vintage pickup to resume the demands of the day. We resumed our work as well, devising elaborate schemes to capture acorns beyond our reach and cleverness.

We had spent a hard season collecting native seed, often attempting feats of agility and strength that are ill-advised for men of waxing girth and waning youth. That week we concentrated on the Iowa, Missouri, and Nebraska counties along the Missouri River. The eastern deciduous forest follows the river north and west, painting a green hardwood stripe on the Plains—hemmed by tallgrass prairie on either side. We collected seeds from buckeyes, pawpaws, hickories, basswoods, hawthorns, bladdernuts, hop-hornbeams, and many others, in addition to a variety of oaks. Each of these is a tough frontier cousin of eastern kin, often growing in isolated pockets and hard-to-reach habitats.

Of course it would have been much easier to buy some trees. But high-quality native trees of local provenance can be very difficult to find in commerce. Ironically, it is often easier to buy a tree from another country than one that is native to your own county. And to that irony we can add another: Many conservation and community planting projects rely on exotic trees or "native" trees of distant or unknown origin as a way to improve wildlife habitats or make communities greener. That's like trying to help sandhill cranes by releasing flamingos.

If you want to help the planet, plant wild plants. If you want to have abundant butterflies and birds in your backyard, plant wild plants. If you want a sustainable landscape that requires minimal water, chemicals, and care, plant wild plants. A wild plant is native and grown directly from seeds collected in natural ecosystems in your area. Seasonal rhythms, resilience, and the ability to successfully integrate into local food webs are preserved in wild seeds and saplings. It's not enough to plant a native tree; those that are native, local, and wild do the most good.

Desire for wild seed only partly accounts for our obsession. The other part, at least for me, is an Acorn Ethic. That is, the conviction that the act of planting a wild tree benefits the planter. Planting wildly joins a cascade of energy. The seed or sapling creates a community upon planting; energy gathered by photosynthesis and released through reproduction, consumption, and eventual decay moves through countless bodies and takes many forms. The planter will never see the fullness of this cascade but is nevertheless drawn into it. Kneeling to plant, we are at once humbled and enlivened.

After the kind farmer drove away, we approached our task from every angle. We searched the grove on knees and bellies, finding few acorns and even fewer that were not half-eaten by weevils or squirrels. Most of the trees were taking the year off from reproduction, and the few low-hanging acorns we could reach required viability testing. Some collectors carry a knife to open acorns for visual inspection. I prefer to eat a few; a moist, meaty acorn indicates a viable crop. After a long while, we returned to the lane with just a handful of acorns and an impressive collection of chigger bites.

The long afternoon began to cool. Robert and I had harvested what we could reach (and some that we couldn't), so we resigned ourselves to half-empty buckets and a long drive home. But as we packed up, the kind farmer returned with an enormous tool of his own creation: a sinister-looking steel hook that was twelve feet long. We speculated that it was used either to close a gate while sitting on a tractor or to teach hippie tree huggers a lesson. To our delight, this tool enabled us to risk serious injury even further and to double our reach and take. Our hopes increased with the weight of our haul. The promise of having wild oak saplings next planting season made a good day in the woods even better.

Others who want to plant wildly also have reason for hope. An increasing number of nurseries are growing wild local trees and other native plants, and there may be one in your area. Or better yet, embrace the Acorn Ethic in its purest form by collecting your own seeds. Planting an acorn produces a sturdy oak sooner than you may think, and something wild might germinate in you as well. We will embrace the ethic by returning to those lovely white oaks to collect and to entertain a farmer when the acorns are ripe. Robert can use his new hook.

# The Natural Calendar at Wilderness Park

*By* Linda R. Brown

One day in late March or early April the sandhill cranes in the Platte Valley feel the lift of warm south winds. They rise on thermals and leave Nebraska. Their departure marks, for me, the beginning of spring in Wilderness Park. I begin a series of almost weekly walks through the Saltillo Road portion of this "wildy" city park running at least ten miles along the Salt Creek floodplain on the southwestern edge of Lincoln. Through the years there have been both early and late springs. Still, on every walk I make new discoveries. I am a birder, so I am always hoping for the arrival of a new migrant. For this article, I would like to share with you my journal entry of a walk I made in Wilderness Park in the spring of 2009.

Today is March 29, 2009. It is fifty-four degrees, and it is sunny. An email from Omaha told me the spring beauties are blooming in Fontenelle Forest. A friend and I drive south on South 27th to

Saltillo Road, turn west, cross the railroad track, and turn right into the Wilderness Park parking lot. I have seen first-blooming dog's-tooth violets in this section of the woods, but never spring beauties. We start along the paths, hoping to see some. The openness of this early spring forest impresses us. No new growth blocks the view. We hear American robins, black-capped chickadees, northern flickers, and unfamiliar frogs. The frog's upward trill is like the sound made when running a finger along a fine-toothed comb. Later I listened to Nebraska frog sounds on the Internet and identified them as belonging to western chorus frogs. An unfamiliar orange-colored butterfly flits across the path. A Carolina wren repeatedly utters its strident song in the distance.

I have taken friends to this portion of Wilderness Park and have been surprised at how being in such an undeveloped forest leaves some of them feeling lost and anxious. I try to calm them by telling them that it will not be long before another coal train will pass by on the east side of the park. The dogs kenneled along the highway to the southwest bark often enough to keep us oriented. I might add to this the knowledge that the Jamaica North bike trail is on the west side of the park. We can't get lost.

We come to the area that is still an open savanna, cleared when the gas pipeline was laid across the park. Some of the area is covered in a nice large patch of kelly-green monocots. They look like domestic plants, but I can't place them. Perhaps they were planted by the people who once lived in the remnant structure with the fallen chimney. We are headed toward the bridge that Curt Donaldson built. Flies are out today. I think phoebes would like to eat these flies! I wonder if the eastern phoebes are back to claim their regular nesting site under the bridge.

When some other hikers tell us that the herons are on nests in the heron rookery, we switch trails and cross the open, reclaimed prairie. Some years ago the Lincoln Parks Department people recognized a nice group of young native bur oak trees. Realizing this was an opportunity, they brought in bulldozers to clear out the brush and other trees that were crowding the oaks. Now I notice that several of these slender, rather tall bur oaks on the west end of the meadow are twisted, torn, and bent over. Was there a freak windstorm or did the new access to sunlight allow them to grow tall faster than their slender trunks could bear? It is another question to ponder.

Back at the edge of the woods to the north of the meadow, we stand in the sun looking at what may be a deer lay-down. The six-foot circle is covered with deer hair, reminding me of a shedding dog's bed. Later we find the pelvic bone of a deer. Small teeth marks of mice suggest that the calcium in that deer's bones will be used to build strong bones in the next litter of baby mice. The gully formed by Salt Creek looks well scoured. The water must rush along its muddy banks often. No bushes have been able to take hold. Only bur oak leaves cover the muddy bottom. I hear a new bird call: Beep, beep, beep—deedle, deedle, dedder, deedle, deep. Because of the three preliminary notes, I think it must be a song sparrow. We see a red-bellied woodpecker on the top of a newly formed snag. There is a good hole in the underside of a south-facing dead branch below his high perch. We look for landmarks that would help us relocate this probable nesting site.

Moving on, I catch a glimpse of two huge birds in flight. It takes me a moment to realize that these must be the great blue herons. Sure enough, we find four herons standing on small, incipient nests. We wonder if there are enough fish in Salt Creek to support a nesting colony of great blue herons. We know we are not far from a substantial colony of great blues that seem to do well. We move away, not wanting to disturb them.

A bit farther we see another orange butterfly. This is probably the fourth one we have seen. This time I take pictures. The digital images help me find this butterfly in Kaufman's *Field Guide to Butterflies of North America*. It is an eastern comma in winter form. We wonder what it is feeding on because we have not seen any flowers blooming.

I hear a bird muttering close by. I am surprised when I find it is a white-breasted nuthatch. It is working the tree in its usual upside-down position, but the little contact sounds are different from the expected "yank yank" call. I hear the rattle of another red-bellied woodpecker. His sound reminds me of the belted kingfishers we often find feeding in Salt Creek. I walk off the path to see if the phoebe might be under a nearby railroad bridge. Instead of the phoebe, I find large hollow bones. I carry the bones back to my friend, who, because of the large spur on the tarsus, pronounces this skeleton to be that of a male turkey.

We did not find spring beauties, but we left with the hope of more discoveries to come. They always do in Wilderness Park.

# Birding Lake McConaughy

*By* STEPHEN J. DINSMORE

---

Situated at the base of the Nebraska Panhandle, the Lake Mc-
Conaughy area is one of the premier birding areas in Nebraska
and the entire Great Plains region. Much of this is a result of the
diversity of habitats in this small area—a large lake with sandy
beaches, lush marshes, riparian habitat along major river corri-
dors, extensive thickets of cedars, the Sandhills grasslands, and
urban areas. Ornithologists and birders visiting this area have
documented an incredible 365 species of birds, largely a result of
the habitat diversity.

Generally, there are four locales that provide a good overview
of the birds of this region. The 14,400-hectare Lake McConaughy
is the largest lake in Nebraska and contains more than 160 ki-
lometers of shoreline. The main lake hosts waterfowl, loons,
grebes, gulls, and terns while the shoreline is favored by shorebirds, and the ribbon of forest along the lakeshore hosts many
nesting and migrant songbirds. A spotting scope is necessary to

see birds on the lake, but wind, fog, and heat shimmer can make it challenging to see birds in the middle. Good birding spots are the pullouts at either end of Kingsley Dam, Lakeview (Van's) on the south shore, and Arthur Bay, Lemoyne, and Cedar Vue on the north shore. Below Kingsley Dam are Lakes Ogallala and Keystone (actually just a single body of water), which combine to form a smaller, sheltered lake with some marsh and surrounding forest. The lake is home to waterfowl and huge numbers of gulls. Bald eagles favor the trees along the edge, and the forested areas can be excellent for migrant songbirds. Good birding spots are the eagle-viewing building near the spillway, the campground at the northeast end of the lake, the foot trail along the south shore of the lake, and the riparian areas immediately below the Keystone diversion dam at the east end of the lake. At the opposite (west) end of Lake McConaughy lie the extensive Clear Creek marshes, best accessed off Highway 92 from the Keith County line west to Highway 26 or from Road 44 heading east from Highway 26 along the south side of the marshes. The wetlands are home to migrant waterfowl and sandhill cranes, nesting bitterns, rails, and other marsh birds, while the surrounding meadows and sandhills host many migrant and wintering raptors and nesting grassland birds. Finally, Ash Hollow State Historical Park is accessed from Highway 26 just south of the Clear Creek marshes and is a good place to find forest-nesting birds and migrant songbirds.

The bird diversity of the Lake McConaughy area varies seasonally, with a peak occurring in April-May and again in August-September; diversity is lowest in January-February. Some birds are resident year-round while others may only appear for a week or two at a particular season. An awareness of the seasonal occurrence of birds in this region will greatly enhance your ability to find certain species.

One of the primary avian spectacles is the annual migration of waterfowl through this area. Spring migration is often underway by mid-February with the arrival of geese, northern pintails, and many diving ducks. The first spring migrants seek open water that is usually present at Lake Ogallala or at the west end of Lake McConaughy. Spring numbers and diversity peak in March and decline rapidly in April. A few species breed locally, most notably redheads and ruddy ducks. The autumn migration begins in August with the arrival of flocks of blue-winged teal and peaks in October–November. Hunting pressure alters the use pattern during fall, although Lake Ogallala is a consistent viewing spot. This is also the season to look for less common visitors like scoters and long-tailed ducks. As the lakes begin to freeze in December, the birds will become concentrated at the east end of Lake McConaughy and in the open water on Lake Ogallala. Diving ducks predominate, including tens of thousands of common mergansers and the occasional Barrow's goldeneye. Mid-winter is a good time to look for wintering trumpeter swans, especially along the North Platte River below Keystone dam, on Lake Ogallala, and in deeper bays along the north shore of Lake McConaughy.

Besides waterfowl, many other waterbirds visit the region. Small numbers of common loons frequent Lakes McConaughy and Ogallala in April and again in October–November, with the occasional bird oversummering. Lake McConaughy is one of the most important mid-continent staging sites for western grebes, with September–October counts reaching thirty thousand birds some years! A few Clark's grebes, along with small numbers of horned and eared grebes, are present during April–May and September–November. American white pelicans flock by the hundreds to shallow-water areas in migration, especially in April and September. Great blue herons nest in small colonies in trees near water, while other wading birds, including the secretive American bittern and white-faced ibis, are regular migrants in wet areas with emergent vegetation. Shorebirds, one of the more diverse groups of birds in this region (thirty-six regular species), are primarily migrants that prefer shallow water with adjacent exposed mud. Thousands may be present when habitat conditions are good, but they are scarce in other years. Lake McConaughy's sandy beaches support internationally important numbers of nesting piping plover, which, along with the least tern, are among the most imperiled birds in this region. Long-billed curlews and upland sandpipers are characteristic nesting birds of the Sandhills. Gulls are another diverse group of birds that occur in this region, and birders have noted many rare species. Check the numerous ring-billed and herring gulls in late fall and winter for California, glaucous, and Thayer's gulls. Thousands of Franklin's gulls occur during migration, and the vastness of Lake McConaughy sometimes attracts migrant jaegers and Sabine's gulls.

This region is home to five resident gallinaceous birds (game birds). Displaying sharp-tailed grouse and greater prairie-chickens perform spectacular spring mating dances (called "booming") in the Sandhills in March and April; both are occasionally seen in other open habitats the rest of the year. The wild turkey is a typical bird of the riparian forest along the lakes and rivers, while the less common northern bobwhite occurs in similar habitat.

Raptors, or birds of prey, are another group of birds for which this region is well known. At the top of the list is the bald eagle, a locally common winter resident with the peak counts in January and February. Eagles can occur anywhere in the region but are best seen loafing on the ice or roosting in trees along the shore of Lake Ogallala. The birds are concentrated here during the coldest winter weather because of the open water and abundant fish that serve as a food source. The Nebraska Central Power and Public Irrigation District has constructed an eagle-viewing building that is open seasonally for viewing. Counts of one hundred or more eagles are possible, and the building offers a comfortable location from which to view the eagles, waterfowl, and gulls in winter. Other raptors abound in the region. Ospreys patrol the lakeshores in April–May and again in September in search of fish. Nesting red-tailed and Swainson's hawks are replaced in winter by rough-legged hawks and the occasional ferruginous hawk, as well as a few merlins and prairie falcons. Northern harriers are a common migrant and irregular winter visitor. All of these birds prefer grasslands, especially those bordering the lakes and rivers. A visit to this same habitat at dusk in winter might produce a sighting of a short-eared owl floating over the grass in search of rodents. The burrowing owl is a rare nester, preferring prairie dog colonies, while long-eared and northern saw-whet owls can be encountered in dense cedar groves in winter. The diminutive loggerhead shrike is a nesting bird with a diet of mostly insects, and in winter is replaced by the larger northern shrike, whose diet is small birds and rodents. Both birds share the nickname "butcherbird."

Other birds, including the diverse songbirds, abound in the Lake McConaughy region and represent about half of its bird diversity. Hillsides with grass and scattered cedars support nesting common poorwills, a nocturnal insectivore at the eastern edge of its range, and other species such as western kingbird, brown thrasher, spotted towhee, and lark sparrow. The thin ribbon of trees along the shore of Lake McConaughy supports many migrant flycatchers, vireos, warblers, and sparrows, especially in April–May and August–October. Typical breeding birds of this habitat include the red-headed woodpecker (currently increasing with the drought-related die-off of cottonwoods), western wood-pewee, warbling vireo, tree swallow, house wren, orchard oriole, and American goldfinch. Shallow marshes and the adjacent shrubs and willow thickets, including those at Clear Creek and Lake Ogallala, support nesting willow flycatcher, marsh wren, yellow warbler, and red-winged and yellow-headed blackbirds. A trip into the grassy Sandhills during the nesting season could produce loggerhead shrike, horned lark, lark bunting, grasshopper sparrow, and western meadowlark. And finally, generalist breeding birds include the eastern kingbird, cliff swallow, common yellowthroat, and song sparrow. The region is also a zone of contact between birds whose ranges lie mostly to the east or west—western and eastern wood-pewees, rose-breasted and black-headed grosbeaks, lazuli and indigo buntings, and Baltimore and Bullock's orioles, all of which occur, including a few hybrid individuals!

This is by no means a thorough coverage of the area, which supports more than 360 species of birds. If you have any interest in birds, this is an area worth exploring at any season. Who knows, you might get lucky and discover a regional first!

# Escape to the River

*By* MATT GERSIB

---

In a world that works so hard to stay connected every minute of the day, there's something amazingly calming about the escape that can be found on the meandering flow of Nebraska's waterways. The kids don't have to fuss about what's happening on their favorite social networking site. There's no need to worry about mowing the lawn or whether the stock market went up—because when you're on the river, it's all about your family, your canoe, the water, and the environment around you. It's time to take it all in.

Portions of ten of Nebraska's most popular paddling rivers have been established as designated canoe trails in conjunction with the American Canoe Association's water trails initiative. The Nebraska canoe trail segments have been chosen because they represent the beauty and majesty of the respective rivers they are a part of. They are perfect for recreational use by families looking for a great adventure lasting up to five days along eighteen to seventy-two miles of river.

The Nebraska Game and Parks Commission has published online guides for each of the ten canoe trails in Nebraska. Each guide includes general information about the river, canoe trail put-in and take-out points, and areas of interest, as well as the locations of public and private campsites, picnic and restroom facilities, and contact information for local community and medical authorities along the route.

The commission has also published an overall *Nebraska Canoe Trails Guide* that includes general information about Nebraska's rivers and canoe trails, along with tips for a successful float. The guide includes a statewide listing of outfitters offering canoe rentals, shuttle services, and, in some cases, guide services. The Niobrara River, in particular, features an abundance of outfitters ready to serve paddlers because of that river's popularity with families and recreation groups.

Nebraska's canoe trails are excellent for family paddling, as their waters flow slow and gentle. In fact the International Scale of Difficulty generally rates Nebraska's rivers at Class I: Easy; moving water with small waves and riffles can be expected, with few obstacles. The Niobrara River in north-central and northeastern Nebraska features some faster moving water, rapids, and chutes, which keeps the trip entertaining for experienced paddlers yet manageable for families and beginning paddlers.

## The Niobrara River Canoe Trail

Without a doubt, the Niobrara River offers some of the most fun and challenging water to paddle in Nebraska. Stretching across northern Nebraska from a narrow, shallow beginning in eastern Wyoming, this National Scenic River features an incredible assortment of waterfalls, rapids, and chutes. It's the combination of these elements that makes the 30.5-mile Niobrara River Canoe Trail one of the premier paddling locales in the nation for canoe and kayak enthusiasts alike.

This canoe trail begins at the Cornell Bridge at Fort Niobrara National Wildlife Refuge and travels in an easterly direction. A daily access fee is charged at the launch, and a sticker must be affixed to your canoe or kayak. The Niobrara River Canoe Trail ends at the Norden Bridge, which is located south of the village of Norden.

Out on the water the Niobrara River Canoe Trail offers almost immediate options for scenery, courtesy of trails shooting off from the sides of the river that lead to secluded spots like Fort Falls and the overlook at Buffalo Bridge. Some access points, such as the one at Berry Bridge, are private property, and landowners may charge a nominal access and parking fee. Less than ten miles into the journey, Smith Falls State Park offers picnicking, camping, modern restrooms, and showers. It's also the location of the state's highest waterfall, Smith Falls, where water takes a dramatic seventy-foot drop from the top of the birch-lined canyon before making a short journey to the river. It's a must-see for any family traveling down the river.

## The Calamus River Canoe Trail

Flowing gently to its eventual destination at the Calamus Reservoir State Recreation Area, the fifty-six-mile Calamus River Canoe Trail could very well be one of Nebraska's most scenic canoeing stretches. The Nebraska Game and Parks Commission has given the segment from Nebraska Highway 7 bridge to the Calamus Reservoir SRA official canoe trail status, and it stands as one of the state's most diversely beautiful and fun-to-navigate waterways. Its tight turns and tall reeds even create a maze-like feel at times.

Even during the hottest months of the year the Calamus River flows cold and clear since it's fed by the underlying Ogallala Aquifer through a series of artesian wells and springs. This makes the Calamus good for paddling virtually anytime the weather is warm enough. And with low, gently rolling banks along the river providing excellent views of the surrounding Nebraska Sandhills, it's a breathtaking adventure.

## The Republican River Canoe Trail

At a leisurely two-mile-per-hour float from its start at the Harlan County Lake Dam near Republican City, the Republican River Canoe Trail takes paddlers on a winding journey through some of south-central Nebraska's most beautiful country—where wildlife are abundant and people are not. The Republican River is affected by seasonal flows, making July and August optimal times to visit due to water releases common during those months. Contact a local outfitter serving the Republican River or the Corps of Engineers at Republican City to verify water release levels during your planned vacation times. This will help ensure your family has a great paddling experience on the river.

## Tips for Paddling in Nebraska

You may encounter some obstacles that require portage, including low bridges, fences, and low water levels. When encountering a bridge or fence crossing, it is typically best to stop, plan your passage, and, if necessary, get out of your canoe to either walk it under or portage it around the fence. It is critical that fences and bridges are not disturbed as they are essential to ranch and farm operation and are private property.

Only the water in the rivers is public property. The riverbeds and all adjacent lands are private property, so always respect the property and rights of landowners. Nebraska statute gives paddlers permission to portage around fences and other obstructions; however, you are responsible for any damage to the property. Any picnicking or camping on private property should only be done with landowner permission.

In Nebraska, each occupant of a canoe or kayak must have a US Coast Guard-approved Type I, II, III, or IV life preserver on board. Occupants under thirteen years of age must wear an approved life preserver of suitable size at all times.

Nebraska's canoe trails offer a unique opportunity for paddlers to experience some of the best, most scenic segments of the state's premier rivers. So pack up your family and load the canoe. It's time to hit the water!

## Resources

American Canoe Association

Nebraska Division of Travel and Tourism (Visit this site for excellent information on canoeing outfitters, destinations and more.)

Nebraska Game and Parks Commission (For the "Nebraska Canoe Trails Guide," select the Boating tab and click on Canoe Guides in the left-hand navigation.)

National Park Service, Niobrara National Scenic River

# The World Looks Different from the Middle of a Lake

*By* TOM LYNCH

---

The branch of a mulberry tree hangs over the parking lot, dangling ripe berries to within easy reach. I pluck a few, taste the seedy, mildly tart pulp. It's a humid morning, overcast, warm but not oppressive. The threat of a storm hangs in the heavy clouds, but it doesn't feel imminent. The air is still, with only the slightest breeze to shake the mulberry leaves, to ruffle the surface of the nearby lake I've come to drift upon at Olive Creek State Recreation Area.

I unpack my bright yellow inflatable kayak from its plastic tub, roll it out on the parking lot gravel. Doing this, I always check for broken glass first. Smashed beer bottles are an all too common spoor of local knuckleheads. Then I use an electric pump that plugs into my van's cigarette lighter, and within a few minutes the kayak is pumped up and ready to go.

I piece the paddle together, tighten its joints, don my life jacket, and I'm set. I heft the lightweight kayak over to the boat launch.

A few years ago my wife and I had purchased a canoe, and we pictured ourselves out every weekend, intrepid voyagers on the lakes and rivers of Nebraska. And we did use it a few times, but not as much as we'd expected. It was just too hard to get its heavy, awkward bulk onto and off the top of our vehicle. So one year, I think it was for Mother's Day, I bought her an inexpensive and very lightweight inflatable kayak. She loved it. It was just the thing for the kind of casual paddling on local lakes we were really inclined to do. Soon, I'd bought my own, a different, larger model. Mine's billed as being a two-person craft, and that's true, it does come with two seats. But it's mighty cramped, especially for the paddler in the rear, whose jutting knees interfere with paddling. So we normally use it as a single seater.

I set the kayak down into the water. Now comes the hard part, getting myself into it with some degree of grace and dignity. Sometimes when I'm getting in the shore is lined with fishermen, all of whom turn their gaze my direction. Under such scrutiny, I try hard not to take an ungainly tumble but instead to look like a competent outdoorsman. This can be hard to fake. Thankfully there's no audience today as I settle myself into the shaky seat.

With my paddle, I push away from shore, drift through patches of bright green algae and a dead catfish only just beginning to stink. Fortunately, the water gets more pleasant away from shore. I wonder if this algae is the kind that makes our lakes so toxic. The Nebraska Department of Environmental Quality website says that the toxic algae has "a neon green, pea green, blue-green or reddish-brown color." Hah, that really narrows it down, doesn't it. Today, I'm not worried, but the effects of this algae on local lakes is troubling. A lot of these lakes would be lovely to swim in on a hot summer day, but even if a toxic algae alert hasn't officially been issued, I'm not sure I'd risk it.

To my mind, the causes of these toxic blooms, runoff of fertilizer from nearby farms, hasn't been adequately addressed by local politicians. If a factory put these sorts of contaminants into local waterways, there'd be a crackdown. But agriculture has its own set of rules. Holmes Lake, which has little or no agriculture in its watershed, just lots of lawns, is the one lake where it seems serious efforts are being made to reduce fertilizer runoff. Even still, it's a challenge getting people to reduce fertilizer use in a town with such an entrenched lawn fetish. Maybe if this program is successful, someday we'll be able to swim at Holmes Lake.

I paddle to the middle of the lake, drift in a casual circle, panning the horizon. The quiet is lovely. The far shore's reflection shimmers in the still lake. Even familiar scenery looks interesting and new from this perspective. The world looks different from the middle of a lake.

I paddle south to the marshy areas. In the spring, I've seen lots of shore birds and water birds here—teal, greater yellowlegs, even pelicans—but none are around this far into the summer. Most of those birds have flown off to Canada to nest and breed.

A bit of a breeze comes up, blowing from the north. Given the threat of storm, I fear the wind might stiffen and I'll need to paddle back directly into it, not an easy task. So I decide to head for the north end of the lake. That way, if a storm does come up quickly, its wind will push me in the direction I want to go, back to the boat launch.

I stroke along at a leisurely pace, left, right, left, right. Inflatable kayaks are definitely slower cutting through the water than their hard-shell siblings. And they're not as nimble, either. So if you have a need for speed or plan a lot of whitewater trips, I'd recommend the hard-shell variety. But inflatables are fine for this sort of leisure activity. Be sure to get a skeg, an attachable external fin, or, trust me, you'll spend a lot of time paddling in circles. Generally, though, inflatable kayaks are pretty simple to navigate and control. And there's no need to learn the Eskimo roll. They are hard to dump. But, of course, not impossible. That's what the life jacket is for.

The wind never does pick up but quiets again, and a few drops of rain speckle the lake surface. I paddle into a cove in the northwest corner of the lake, startling a heron up. The water here is still as glass. Drifting twenty feet from shore, I'm in a good location to watch birds in the shoreline trees of ash, locust, and hackberry. A rose-breasted grosbeak perches in a treetop. An eastern kingbird swoops from a branch to snatch a bug over the water then returns to its perch. A catbird mews. Cardinals sing from somewhere out of sight. Red-winged blackbirds cackle in the reeds, while a few swallows circle over the water. Looking at all these birds through binoculars as the kayak drifts, I find myself getting queasy.

A fish breaks the surface nearby. I'm not fishing today, but kayaks make fine craft from which to fish. I've used this one for trout fishing on lakes in Colorado and found it ideal.

As I head back to the boat launch, I swing around a tree snag poking out of the water. Such snags are my biggest concern paddling an inflatable craft on these local lakes. I see myself running into a sharp, submerged branch, tearing a big hole in the bottom, and swimming back to shore. So I give these branches a wide berth. Actually, our kayaks have proven very sturdy, and they've not even sprung a small leak. But there's no need to risk my luck among the snags.

As with most things, you can spend as much money as you're willing to part with for a kayak. Top of the line models can put you out more than two thousand dollars. But since we aren't planning any grand adventures, and since we're tightwads, we got ours for less than $150 each.

Eastern Nebraska has loads of small lakes that are ideal for leisurely kayaking. Mostly we paddle on Holmes Lake, which is near our house, but it's fun to investigate some of the others, farther from home, an impulse that has brought me to Olive Creek this morning. There are also some local rivers that are suitable for kayaks and canoes. Nebraska Game and Parks has an excellent website titled "Nebraska water trails guide" with lots of information on those river trip options.

Someday I might even try one of those trips myself. But today, I lack the ambition for such an adventure and am content to spend an hour or two paddling and drifting, noticing how the world looks different from the middle of a lake.

# Wetlands

*By* JOANNA POPE

---

Wetlands—some call them "wasteland," "nonproduction acres," or simply "a pain in the neck." Don Cox, however, calls them an oasis in a desert of cropland for wildlife to find rest, food, and a place to call home.

Cox calls Adams County home. Adams County is located in the heart of a unique geographic area known as the Rainwater Basin.

The Rainwater Basin is a complex of wetlands that covers portions of twenty-one counties in south-central Nebraska. The Rainwater Basin area is the narrowest portion of the migration route known as the Mid-Continental Flyway. In the spring, birds that have wintered on the Gulf Coast and across Texas and Mexico funnel into this 150-mile-wide area that contains several hundred wetlands covering about twenty-one thousand acres.

The wetlands within the Rainwater Basin provide the perfect habitat for migrating water birds. Rainwater Basin wetlands are

shallow, elliptical depressions lined with a relatively imperme-
able layer of clay. These wetlands provide the food and habitat
critical for migrating birds to ensure they arrive at the northern
nesting grounds in prime condition for breeding.

From mid-February to mid-March, millions of waterfowl
use the wetlands and uplands of the Rainwater Basin Region
of Nebraska for resting, feeding, and pair-bond formation. The
numbers are impressive: three to six million snow geese, four
million mallards, nine hundred thousand white-fronted geese,
nine hundred thousand pintails, plus millions of other migrating birds, including Canada geese and shorebirds. South-central
Nebraska is also one of the most frequent stopover areas for
whooping cranes on their spring and fall migrations.

The Rainwater Basins are also home to numerous birds and
wildlife throughout the year, including pheasant, blue-winged
teal, mallards, kildeer, American avocets, northern harriers, and
yellow-headed blackbirds.

Despite being critical to migrating and residential wildlife
species, the Rainwater Basin wetlands have been greatly reduced from their historic numbers. Throughout much of the
twentieth century, wetlands were drained for farming, bisected
by roads, or silted-in by erosion, until only about 10 percent of
the original Rainwater Basin wetlands remain.

To help reverse this trend, in 1992 a group of conservation
agencies and organizations formed the Rainwater Basin Joint
Venture. The goal of the Rainwater Basin Joint Venture is to
restore and permanently protect thirty-seven thousand acres
of high-quality wetlands and twenty-five thousand acres of

associated uplands with adequate water and distribution to meet the habitat needs of waterfowl and other migratory birds.

The Joint Venture provides partnership structure for agencies, nongovernmental organizations, landowners, and farmers to address natural resource issues through projects that also improve migratory bird habitat. From its inception, conservation organizations, private citizens, business, and industry have been equal partners with state and federal wildlife agencies in this Joint Venture. Providing incentives for landowners to manage their land for waterfowl has been the key to its success.

Cox is one of the landowners the Rainwater Basin Joint Venture worked with on a large wetland restoration project just north of Hastings, Nebraska. As an avid hunter and waterfowl enthusiast, Cox was well aware of the sharp decline in the number of wetlands within the Rainwater Basin. He wanted to do his part to help improve habitat for migrating birds.

In February 1995 the Rainwater Basin Joint Venture held the first landowner meeting in an attempt to help mediate a solution to water issues in a large wetland area known as the Trumbull Basin. Twenty-five local landowners and farmers attended, along with representatives from various conservation agencies and organizations.

The Trumbull Basin is a six-hundred-acre wetland located within the Rainwater Basin. For many years landowners had tried to farm Trumbull Basin. To deal with the large amount of water flowing into the area after rain events, farmers pumped water off crop ground into pits to later use for irrigation. Dikes were also built around the perimeter of the properties to keep the water from flooding their cropland. Despite these efforts, cropland was often flooded and crop yields compromised as a result

In March 2002 Cox and two partners, Jeff Anderson and Larry Rouse, purchased a quarter section of the Trumbull Basin property at auction with the intent of restoring the wetland. Rouse had farmed the property for the previous thirty years and knew full well the challenges that existed in attempting to get a crop off the property each year. In addition, two adjacent property owners also decided to restore their portions of Trumbull Basin back to wetlands.

The US Department of Agriculture's Natural Resources Conservation Service, a key partner in the Rainwater Basin Joint Venture, worked with the landowners to help them restore their wetlands through the Wetlands Reserve Program. The Wetlands Reserve Program is a voluntary program offering landowners the opportunity to protect, restore, and enhance wetlands on their property.

Through the Wetlands Reserve Program, the Natural Resources Conservation Service provides technical and financial support to help landowners with their wetland restoration efforts. WRP provides landowners the choice whether to enroll their property into a ten-year, thirty-year, or permanent easement.

Once the land is enrolled into the program, landowners may no longer use the land to produce a crop, but they have many other options available. There are several compatible uses for which landowners may continue to use the restored wetland, including haying, grazing, and recreation. NRCS will work with landowners to develop a "compatible use agreement" as long as the activity does not compromise the ability of the property to function fully as a wetland.

The goal of the NRCS is to achieve the greatest wetland functions and values, along with optimum wildlife habitat, on every acre enrolled in the Wetlands Reserve Program. This program offers landowners an opportunity to establish long-term conservation and wildlife practices and protection.

"The goals of the Wetlands Reserve Program met our goals perfectly. We wanted to create the best wetland out there, and the Wetlands Reserve Program provided us the technical and financial assistance to make that happen," Cox said.

Cox and his partners enrolled their property into the permanent easement option under the Wetlands Reserve Program. NRCS developed a wetland restoration plan with the help of other Rainwater Basin Joint Venture partners, which included the Nebraska Game and Parks Commission and the US Fish and Wildlife Service.

The restoration plan restored the hydrology of the wetland. It called for the removal of over 150,000 cubic yards of sediment that had washed into the wetland after the years of farming as well as for the removal of all perimeter dikes. The soil excavated from the wetland was used to help build up the county road adjacent to the project area. Several culverts were removed or relocated to help prevent water from leaving the wetland and equalize water levels on the various properties. Several new culverts were added to help drain water off neighboring property into the newly restored wetland. On the upland acres surrounding the wetland a mix of native grasses were planted, providing additional wildlife habitat.

The restoration project took nearly a year, but Cox and his partners have been extremely pleased with the results.

"Although our primary goal for enrolling the property in WRP was to benefit waterfowl, as a result of the restoration pheasants, quail, deer, and many other types of wildlife have been direct benefactors," Cox said.

Shanda Weber, resource conservationist with NRCS in the Hastings field office, works with Cox and his partners to help them manage the restored wetland. She said their restored wetland is one of the best in the area. She attributes that to their strong desire to take care of the wetland. Management of the wetland has included spraying for noxious weeds, conducting prescribed burns, and disking to help control reed canary grass and other invasive vegetation.

The Nature Conservancy, through a grant received from the Nebraska Environmental Trust, recently helped with cost share to build a fence around the restored portions of the Trumbull Basin wetlands. Ducks Unlimited provided technical expertise for fencing specifications and design and oversaw construction of the fencing. Cattle will soon be moved onto the property to graze the wetland under a specific grazing plan approved by the NRCS. Grazing is another wetland management tool used to help enhance wetland habitat.

Weber said, "It is so nice to have a landowner dedicated to the management of a wetland. Too often people want to restore a wetland but don't understand that it takes constant management to keep the wetland functioning as it should."

Cox and his partners are proud of the role they have played in helping to restore a wetland.

"This was the perfect opportunity to make a quick, permanent impact on available wetland acres in the Rainwater Basin for migrating waterfowl," Cox said.

# PART IV

## Plants and Animals

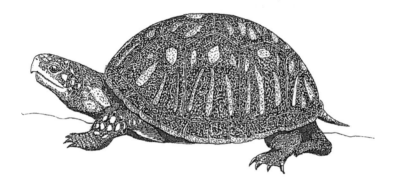

Ornate box turtle (*Terrapene ornata*), adult

# The Turtles of Nebraska

*By* ALAN J. BARTELS

---

Nebraskans are fortunate to have a wide variety of turtles to observe. They occupy most habitats throughout the state. From the arid west and the Sandhills to the wetlands of the Rainwater Basin and the mighty Missouri River in the east, these ancient survivors continue to add to their 230-million-year-old story.

Unfortunately, it is only recently in geologic history that turtles of the world are facing a largely uncertain future. Many turtle species have gone extinct in recent decades. Many more are facing this same fate. These animals that are generally considered the slow pokes of nature can't evolve quickly enough to compete with the rapid pace of human-induced habitat destruction, overharvesting for food and for the pet trade, introduced predators, and our toxic pollution.

Even here in the wildlife-rich state of Nebraska, several of our nine species of chelonians are crawling along a fine line between maintaining the status quo and sinking quietly into oblivion. Regulations passed recently in Nebraska have awarded our turtles legal protections dependent on species, which range from regulated harvest of some species as game animals to protections that make it illegal to possess others.

For many years I provided educational turtle programs to schools, scout groups, summer camps, and retirement homes, and one thing I have learned is that most Nebraskans don't know much about our turtles. Often what they think they know is based on hearsay and myths handed down from grandpa and dad.

## Species Accounts

**Western Painted Turtle.** Perhaps the best known of Nebraska's turtles is the western painted turtle (*Chrysemys picta belli*), also known as the northern painted turtle. This medium-sized turtle can attain a length of eight to ten inches. Adult females are larger than males, with the male having a longer tail and also longer claws on the forelimbs. These longer claws are used to stimulate the female during courtship (he gently strokes her face with his claws); they also help the usually smaller male to hold on to the female during copulation.

The mating period is largely influenced by the weather. Normally in Nebraska it occurs from late March through April and into May, but mating behavior has been observed throughout the warm weather months. These same parameters can be applied to all of Nebraska's turtle species.

Normally in June the female will lay a clutch of oval-shaped eggs in a flask-shaped depression she will excavate in the ground using her hind limbs. Depending on the size of the female, she may lay up to twenty eggs. Some females will lay more than one clutch annually, and not all females will lay eggs every year. Typical of Nebraska's turtles, most young will emerge after sixty to eighty days. With painted turtles, nests that are laid later in the year may produce young that do not emerge from the nest until the following spring (overwintering).

Most nests don't survive long enough to hatch and will be destroyed by predators such as skunks, opossums, raccoons, coyotes, snakes, insects, some rodents, and even feral cats, among many other predators. The young that emerge from any surviving nests must then run the gauntlet of crows and other predatory birds, as well as the aforementioned predators, as they begin their journey toward aquatic habitat. Once they reach the relative safety of the water they are eaten by several species of fish, including largemouth bass and northern pike, as well as bullfrogs, herons, and occasionally other turtles.

Painted turtles prefer slow-moving or still waters with abundant vegetation. They can be found in natural ponds and lakes, farm ponds, creeks and rivers, sewer ponds, and irrigation ditches. They are omnivorous, meaning they eat both plant and animal matter. They are opportunistic and will eat many species of insects, mosquito larvae, amphibians, and fish, and will also take advantage of any dead animals (carrion) they may happen upon.

Because people are prone to picking turtles up off roads and making them into pets, I offer the following story.

An old woman once brought me a painted turtle and asked that I tell her what was wrong with it. The animal was in a cardboard box along with a rotting hunk of meat. Her complaint was that the animal wouldn't eat and that she'd had it a month. I asked her what she kept it in. She replied, "This box." Imagine her embarrassment when I sternly told her that the turtle was slowly starving to death since it has to be in water in order to swallow food. That animal came home with me and was subsequently rehabilitated and released. My point—if you want to keep turtles, other reptiles, or any animal as a pet, do enough research to provide the animal a healthy existence. I often encourage people who insist on keeping a turtle as a pet to keep it a few days at most and then return it to whence it came.

The top shell or carapace of the painted turtle ranges from olive green to almost black and is often coated with algae. The bottom shell of a turtle is called the plastron. On our painted turtles it is a beautiful red (hence the name "painted turtle") and has a dark blotch in the center. The head and legs are striped with yellow and red. Like all of our aquatic turtles, painted turtles spend the winter underwater, either simply lying on or burrowed into the bottom.

Turtles are not just out wandering aimlessly when they come upon a road. Painted turtles as well as Nebraska's other turtle species are prone to excessive road kills where roads have bisected their natural habitat and migration routes. Especially vulnerable are females who may migrate long distances to find suitable nesting sites. They may travel even farther in areas where nesting sites have been altered by humans. All too often

142

these turtles are struck deliberately as they attempt to cross our busy highways.

If you are inclined to move a turtle off the roadway, always place it off the road in the direction it was going. If not, it will simply attempt to cross again. Only move turtles off the road if it is safe for you to do so. A few years ago a child in the southern US who was trying to move a turtle from the road was killed by oncoming traffic. I know from experience that your spouse will not appreciate it if you run into the road to kick a painted turtle out of the path of an oncoming semitruck. (I kicked it because there was not time to stop, bend down, and pick it up.)

**Ornate Box Turtle.** Another well known species of turtle in Nebraska is the ornate box turtle (*Terrapene ornata*). This is the only fully terrestrial of our turtles, the others being mostly aquatic. It once ranged from the eastern boundary of Nebraska westward throughout most of the state. Due to conversion of habitat to agricultural use as well as roadways, towns, acreages, industrial sites, and other developments, this species is most common now in the Sandhills region where it is able to coexist with ranching. Box turtles still exist in a few other fragmented populations throughout parts of its former range. These extant animals are usually old adults that spend the remainder of their lives existing on the fringes and rarely if ever encounter mates.

They may attain a length of six inches. The shell can close tightly via the use of muscular hinges. This has been compared to a closed box, thus the name "box" turtle. The shell is yellow and brown, and the pattern varies widely from one individual to another. Adult males usually have red eyes.

These turtles lay four to six eggs in the spring. Their diet consists mainly of insects, flowers, some fruits, and carrion. People have observed box turtles scavenging through cattle droppings looking for insects. For thousands of years the same process occurred as bison converted the grass to "prairie coal." This trait is valuable to ranchers as box turtles break up "cowpies" and allow new grass to emerge where the dung was covering the ground. I have encountered many of these turtles beneath mulberry trees, all with purple-stained faces and front feet from gorging themselves on the tasty fruit.

Sadly, many "old-timers" I have spoken to have related to me how very common box turtles were only a few decades ago and how they rarely encounter them nowadays. In some parts of the state the sighting of a box turtle becomes a noteworthy event. Sad indeed.

Formerly, box turtles, as well as other species of reptiles and amphibians, were collected without limit by commercial collectors to be sold for medical research or for food. Others were exported around the country for the pet trade. These animals (and turtles in general) typically do not adapt well to captivity, and most die a slow death at the hands of keepers who do not know the animal's specialized requirements.

**Common Snapping Turtle.** Perhaps the most notorious of Nebraska's turtles is the common snapping turtle (*Chelydra serpentina*). Its aggressive reputation is greatly exaggerated as it is only defensive when captured, molested, or removed from the water. When given a chance, it will avoid human contact altogether. Another exaggerated trait of this animal is its reputation as a killer of waterfowl and game fish. As an opportunistic hunter, it will take these items when the opportunity presents itself; however, studies have indicated that vegetation comprises a large quantity of its normal diet (75 to 90 percent), and even giant snappers eat large quantities of insects and insect larvae. Carrion is an important part of the snapping turtle's diet as well.

The underside of the snapper is unlike any other Nebraska species. Its head and limbs are so large that a larger plastron would make withdrawing into the shell difficult. In addition, with its sharp claws and powerful beak, it has no need for the additional protection that a full shell would provide.

I have observed fisherman catching snappers, cutting off the head or otherwise killing the animal. This unethical behavior is also illegal—snapping turtles are classified as game animals in Nebraska and protected as such. These uneducated fishermen have explained to me that they killed the turtle to protect the game fish population. But a turtle taking advantage of a stringer of struggling fish does not equate to a predator that specializes in fish. Ducks are also not in any particular danger from snappers—hen ducks are very good mothers and sense underwater movement very well; more often than not, they are able to lead their broods to safety. Bass, pike, and invasive bullfrogs are much more lethal predators of ducklings than are snapping turtles. Regardless, this predator-prey interaction has persisted for millions of years, and predators and prey are necessary for a healthy ecosystem.

Some folks consider snapping turtle meat a delicacy. I have heard that the chore of butchering the animal is not worth the little meat that can be obtained from even a large turtle. Others have told me that butchering is not difficult if you know the right way, and this must be the case since the turtle-eating tradition is popular in many parts of the country. A wide variety of companies offer snapper meat for sale over the Internet. Classified as a game animal in Nebraska, the sale of snapping turtle meat, shells, or other products from snappers harvested in Nebraska is illegal.

Although I didn't catch or butcher the animal, I have tried turtle meat. To me it tasted very much like chicken—but not as good. I would prefer a young chicken that quickly reaches eating size to butchering an animal that took decades to accumulate very little meat and is such a chore to butcher.

This long-lived animal occupies the top spot in the Nebraska waters where it occurs. As the top predator, it accumulates all of the toxins absorbed by all the other components of its diet. A study in some of New York state's agricultural areas revealed that snapping turtles that were tested contained levels of toxins (pesticides, herbicides, and industrial chemicals) one thousand times the legal threshold for banning the consumption of fish. People who routinely eat snapping turtles from contaminated streams, ponds, and rivers could be putting their health at risk. Considering the breadth of the agriculture industry in Nebraska and the amount of chemicals used on farm fields, it is likely that our snapping turtles harbor even larger concentrations of chemicals harmful to humans.

The record size for a wild-caught common snapper is seventy-six pounds. I have seen several in Nebraska that weighed over fifty pounds and recently heard of a harvested specimen that weighed seventy-one pounds before it was butchered in northern Nebraska, but I have been unable to authenticate this. These large beasts can inflict serious injury to inexperienced handlers through the use of their sharp beak, claws, and lightning-quick strike. All risk to people can be avoided by simply leaving the animal alone. Just like humans who have been bitten by rattlesnakes, most humans whose bites have been attributed to snapping turtles are men who are bitten on the hand, often while intoxicated. The best advice: Leave the snapper alone!

Up to one hundred eggs have been recorded from a Nebraska specimen but usually around thirty is the norm. They are slightly smaller than a ping-pong ball and about the same shape.

This prehistoric beast is unlikely to be confused with any other turtle in Nebraska. Its spiked tail is reminiscent of the dinosaurs, and the jagged rear edge of the carapace reminds one of a saw blade. Long, pearly claws are evident, and when observed, it is clear this hardy survivor is an evolutionary success and a truly beautiful wonder of our natural world.

One time south of O'Neill, Nebraska, I came upon a pair of well-dressed young women standing in the middle of Highway 281. They were on their way to a wedding. I was on my way to a different wedding. A large snapping turtle was blocking one lane of traffic, and these two ladies were having limited success getting the large female turtle to bite the sock they were putting in front of it. It would bite down and the girls would drag the twenty-pounder a few inches before the snapper let go again. As traffic was backed up, I offered my assistance.

I grabbed the turtle by the tail and moved it into the water-filled ditch on the opposite side. Snappers can be safely carried for short distances in this way by experienced handlers. Novices can also drag the turtle by the tail. I've heard of other people using brooms to usher them from the road or others picking them up with shovels. That's great if you have the compassion to help in a situation like this (thank you, ladies), but keep your personal safety in mind, too.

One of my most cherished moments in educating people about turtles came when I was fishing on the land of a farmer friend of mine from near St. Paul, Nebraska. I caught a nice-sized thirty-pound snapper in his creek and proceeded to take it up to his front porch to show it to him. My friend and his wife, George and Marilyn Wall, took a step back when they saw the huge reptile on their front step. Eventually they came outside and took a look at him. I pointed out some of the biology of the algae- and leech-covered swamp thing and explained its diet and its role in the ecosystem. The nervous turtle lunged for me every time I gave it an opportunity. I told the Walls what a beautiful animal I thought it was. George countered as he said to me, "That is probably the most hideous thing I've ever seen, but I'm glad they are down there living in my creek."

**Spiny Softshell Turtle and Smooth Softshell Turtle.** Perhaps the most bizarre of Nebraska's turtles are the softshells. Nebraska has two species, the spiny softshell turtle (*Apalone spinifera*) and the smooth softshell turtle (*Apalone mutica*). The spiny softshells usually have pointed or rounded projections on the front edge of the carapace. The smooth does not have these projections. This is not a foolproof method of identification since large spiny softshell turtles sometimes have almost nonexistent projections that are reduced with age. The best method of identification for the casual observer is that all spiny softshells have a horizontal ridge in the snorkel-like nostrils, and the smooth softshell turtles never have this.

When trying to positively identify the species you have just found at the end of your fishing line, stay clear of the head and sharp claws. These turtles can strike quickly and repeatedly when removed from the water. The head and neck are very long, and the turtle can reach back over its shell and bite the unknowing captor. When fishing turtle-inhabited waters, exchanging nickel-plated hooks for carbon-steel ones is a must. It is nearly impossible to remove a hook from the throat of a turtle without seriously injuring the animal. Attempting to do so also puts the captor at risk. The digestive juices of turtles will eventually dissolve a carbon-steel hook. The line should be cut as close as safely possibly to the hook and the turtle released. I once caught a softshell turtle near Grand Island that had a treble hook from a previous angler squarely embedded in its throat. It was still actively feeding.

These turtles are sometimes called "pancake" turtles or "leatherbacks" because of their low profile and flexible shell. The leathery shell actually covers a hard shell of bone underneath. Their front limbs are heavily webbed and propel them at a fast rate through the water. They can stay under for extended periods without coming to the surface for air. Many turtle species absorb oxygen from the water through blood vessels close to the skin, but the softshells take this survival skill to a new level—they can absorb oxygen through their cloaca.

The softshells suffer the same fate as snappers, as they are sometimes killed mistakenly for being a threat to fisheries. This turtle's narrow head and neck prevent it from taking large prey. Its diet consists mainly of insects. Mollusks and amphibians are also on the menu. It rarely consumes vegetable matter. The softshells, like all of Nebraska's turtles, contribute to the overall health of their environment by taking advantage of diseased animals as well as dead and decaying animals when available.

Females regularly grow twice the size of the males, sometimes even larger. Both species normally lay fifteen to twenty-three spherical eggs, but thirty-two eggs have been recorded for the spiny softshell turtle and thirty-three for the smooth. Like all turtles, they see movement very well. Softshell turtles can outrun a person on level ground for a short distance. They sometimes bask together by the hundreds on sandbars, their many eyes providing great protection against approaching predators. The slightest movement often sends them scurrying to the water.

These aquatic turtles seem to prefer the moving water of rivers and creeks but are also found in backwater sloughs as well as ponds and lakes near moving water.

When threatened, they can in an instant bury themselves in a sandy river bottom and then move underneath to a different location. A fisherman at a bait shop once told me, "I caught one of those out in the river. It scared me so bad that I cut the line and went home." Sure, they are strange looking, but they are fascinating creatures and nothing to be afraid of.

**False Map Turtle.** A less well known species in Nebraska is the false map turtle (*Graptemys pseudeogeographica*). It is found mainly in the Missouri and Lower Platte River systems. Recently I have observed them in the Niobrara River several miles upstream of its confluence with the Missouri River and also in Ponca Creek and the Niobrara River near Spencer.

At first glance it slightly resembles a painted turtle. Upon closer inspection a prominent ridge is evident down the center of the carapace, a serrated edge at the rear of the carapace, and it lacks the red coloration associated with the *Chrysemys picta* complex. Females grow much larger than the males, so much so that years ago map turtle males and females were classified as different species. The males have longer fore claws and longer tails than females. Clutch size is usually about ten eggs, and sometimes a female may produce more than one clutch per year.

This is one of Nebraska's protected species of turtle. Possession is illegal without a scientific or educational permit from the Nebraska Game and Parks Commission. There are many subspecies of map turtles in the US, and most if not all are suffering population declines due to pollution, damming and channelization of rivers, collection for the pet trade, and habitat destruction.

**Yellow Mud Turtle.** The yellow mud turtle (*Kinosternon flavescens flavescens*) is a shy, diminutive creature. It has a strange distribution in Nebraska. It lives in the Republican River drainage in the southern portion of the state, and for some unknown reason it occurs a great distance away in several counties in the Sandhills. George Hudson's 1940s book *The Amphibians and Reptiles of*

*Nebraska* says, "It appears probable that this species has been introduced into Cherry County since all other records for the state are from the Republican River drainage." However, since that time it has been recorded from several other counties in the Nebraska Sandhills, and it has likely been there for some time.

It rarely exceeds a carapace length of over five inches. Males are larger than females and have a longer, thicker tail with a claw at the tip. The female has a very short tail in comparison. Like the box turtle, the yellow mud turtle also has a hinged plastron that provides some protection from predators, although it cannot close it as tightly.

When captured, these turtles often give off an unpleasant odor that, like the musk turtles of the southern US, has earned this species the nickname of "stinkpot."

Whisker-like barbels are present on the chin. These appendages are sensory organs that detect the vibration of predator or prey, which comes in handy since visual acuity is reduced in their muddy, aquatic habitat. Insects and insect larvae, carrion, and amphibians make up the bulk of its diet with very little vegetation being consumed.

These small turtles are not conspicuous except when they may appear in large numbers on roads following rains. Some years they are active only long enough to mate and lay eggs before going dormant again. A Nebraska zoo once had a pair of these turtles and thought they had been stolen or escaped. But after an absence of over a year, they reappeared. They had simply been underground for that time and emerged again when conditions were right. The zookeeper had been fooled several times over the years by these reclusive animals, which have been known to remain underground for two years at a time. Although this species occurs in many states, it is only the female yellow mud turtles of Nebraska that are known to sometimes bury themselves in the ground along with their eggs.

**Red-Eared Slider.** The red-eared slider (*Trachemys scripta elegans*) is a survivor. Hunted to near extinction in the southeast United States, a law passed in the early 1970s making it illegal to sell turtles less than four inches long all but stopped the collection of the species from the wild. It has made a tremendous comeback.

As a result of commercial turtle farms this species is now sold around planet Earth for the food and pet trade. Individual turtle farms in the United State produce in excess of one million hatchlings annually. For children and most people, pet turtles soon lose their novelty—especially after having gone through the chore of cleaning their tanks repeatedly and often. These turtles are often released. Others escape. This hardy, adaptive species has now established itself, by way of human hand, in Germany and Japan. In Taiwan these turtles are released as part of religious ceremonies and are now breeding there.

Why would turtles be imported to Taiwan only to be released later? Because many of Asia's turtle species have already been trapped and eaten to extinction. Others hover precariously close to the brink. It is a lesson those of us in the US should take note of. In France, red-eared sliders outcompete that country's only species of freshwater turtle for food and prime nesting spots. The French turtle is becoming rare as a result.

In Nebraska this omnivore's known native range is the southeastern part of the state in the Missouri River and the Lower Platte. Lazy pet owners have created a breeding population in Lincoln ponds as well as in a few sandpit lakes near Columbus. And it likely exists in other metropolitan areas of Nebraska. Though similar in shape to the painted turtles, the red-eared slider grows much larger. As its common name implies, it typically has a red stripe behind its eye. The stripe is rarely yellow or orange, and the length of the carapace can approach twelve inches. Sexual dimorphism is similar but even more pronounced than in painted turtles. This species and many close relatives occupy the southeast United States. In warmer climates, these turtles may lay eggs three or more times each year (five has been recorded). In Nebraska, one clutch is the norm.

**Blanding's Turtle.** This species largely influenced my desire to educate people about turtles. I found my first Blanding's turtle (*Emydoidea blandingii*) near the Elkhorn River when I was a child. These beautiful turtles with their black and yellow smiley face became my favorite chelonian. I moved away, finished school, and joined the military. When I returned to that secluded spot on the Elkhorn years later, I found my secret swamp drained and the beloved turtles gone. I began researching the species and found that similar habitat destruction was driving it to extinction across the nation.

Fossil evidence indicates that Blanding's turtles likely evolved in what is now Nebraska and then spread south, north and east. Iowa, South Dakota, and Missouri have populations of Blanding's turtles. Minnesota's numbers are second only to

Nebraska's. They also exist in smaller, usually fragmented populations east to Illinois, New York, and Maine, as well as even Nova Scotia, Canada. While Blanding's turtle populations in central and eastern Nebraska are small and fragmented in places due to habitat conversion, the species' stronghold in the state and on the planet exists in locations in the Sandhills because most of the natural marshes and wetlands there have not been drained as they have been in other areas. The fact that they evolved in Nebraska and still thrive in parts of the state is something for residents to be proud of.

The common names of most of our turtles can be deduced by looking at the turtle—mud turtles live in muddy areas (sometimes, but so do other turtles!), painted turtles have those gorgeous colors, softshells have soft shells, and snappers snap (so do others), but what is a Blanding? Actually, the common name for this turtle is shared with the last name of the man credited for first describing it to science. William Blanding was a Pennsylvania physician and naturalist. Although he gets the credit, the species was of course known to the Native Americans throughout its range, its bones and shell fragments having been found in the remains of their early camps. In some areas of the state the Blanding's turtle is misidentified as a mud turtle.

These turtles are extremely long lived. One Blanding's turtle captured as an adult and well cared for lived for another seventy-seven years! It is likely that century-old examples of this species inhabit the rivers and marshes. Research has shown that these turtles routinely hibernate in the same places year after year. Many of these turtles then migrate to a specific pond to feed and mate—the same one annually—then lay their eggs in the same place as in previous years. Considering that some of these turtles predate our road system—and considering that they migrate to the same places each year—it's no wonder these and other species of turtle experience such high mortality on our roadways. Essentially, we built roads through their migration routes.

Recent installation of fencing that directs turtles to culverts that funnel them safely under roads have been very successful in reducing turtle mortality on some stretches of highway in the Sandhills. Though seen as an expensive waste of money by some, should scores of century-old animals be needlessly decimated as we hurry to and fro in our gas-guzzling, polluting conveyances? I think not, and I believe it is money well spent. Any animal spared is one more that can perpetuate the species for future generations, and a world without turtles would be a lonely place indeed. The cost to prevent a species from becoming endangered is far less that the cost of trying to bring one back from the brink.

Blanding's turtles are omnivores but eat mostly insects. Beetles are a staple, and they consume crayfish, amphibians, and carrion when available. This is the only Nebraska species with a bright yellow throat. The carapace is usually black (rarely brown) with yellow dots or bars. The plastron can be mostly black or mostly yellow, but most individuals will be yellow with thumb-shaped black bars along the margin. Males grow to be slightly larger than females. As many as twenty-two eggs have been recorded for a single clutch.

These solar-powered beasts are said to be very cold tolerant. They can creep out of an icy marsh and into a sunny spot and elevate their body temperature at least forty degrees warmer than the air temperature. Like all turtles they are cold blooded and need the energy from the sun (or a warm asphalt road, unfortunately) in order to gain the energy for daily living. Lack of these conditions forces them underwater during winter, where they slow down their bodily functions and patiently exist until spring. Blanding's turtles have been observed swimming under the ice, and radio-tagged animals have revealed that they can move about frequently under the frozen surface of a pond without having to take a breath. Occasionally they have been known to survive the winter under logs or underground.

Though they will hiss and even urinate when startled, these turtles rarely bite. I was fortunate enough to do some volunteer work with this species under the guidance of Dr. Jeff Lang at a wildlife refuge in the Sandhills. Over 1,500 of these animals were captured and marked in two years of fieldwork. Never did one attempt to bite me. We encountered some that had one or two limbs missing after presumably losing them to predators. Others appeared to have survived prairie fires and were horribly scarred. One I recall had a front right limb and flesh up to its elbow missing; a clean and complete white bone remained. Others had survived encounters with automobiles and kept plodding along. These beautiful animals, these Nebraska originals, are survivors.

And they all are. After persisting for so many millions of years, should any species of turtle perish at the hand of a creature as relatively recent as humans? We've altered their world more in the last one hundred years than nature has in the last ten thousand. We've lost many species of turtle on this planet in recent decades, and many more teeter on the brink. Will Nebraska serve as a model of conservation for the rest of the planet? In many ways we already have. But in others we are among the worst offenders.

Education is the key. I know people will protect what they appreciate, what they know about. I hope you've learned something from this article. And now, since you now know something about our turtles—what will you do?

# Swallows along the Platte

## *What the Cliff Swallows of Western Nebraska Have Taught Us about Animal Social Life*

*By* CHARLES R. BROWN

---

As spring slowly gives way to summer along Nebraska's Platte River, and the vast flocks of sandhill cranes and snow geese become only distant memories as they wing their way north to breeding grounds in Canada, Alaska, or Siberia, another avian spectacular unfolds near the braided, winding channels of this storied river. Small, sparrow-sized cliff swallows (*Petrochelidon pyrrhonota*) begin returning in the thousands to form enormous nesting colonies underneath bridges over the Platte, in concrete culverts beneath the highways and railroads that crisscross the river valley, or on riverfront cliff faces and natural outcroppings that line the upper reaches of the North Platte River in far western Nebraska. With their gourd-shaped mud nests clustered closely together, neighboring pairs raise their young as a gigantic synchronous horde, which in some ways more resembles a colony of ants or social bees rather than birds. Cliff swallows rival even the more famous sandhill cranes in their propensity to live in large groups and do everything together.

Sometimes confused with the related barn swallow, cliff swallows are known by their orange rump, square tail, and white forehead patch. The species breeds across most of North America but is more common in the western half of the continent. Migrating to northern Argentina, Uruguay, and southwestern Brazil for the winter, cliff swallows have among the longest migratory journeys of any North American land bird. They are also famous as the swallows that mythically return to California's San Juan Capistrano on March 19, St. Joseph's Day, each year. Cliff swallows historically built their nests underneath vertical ledges on the sides of steep cliffs and canyons in mountainous areas. But relatively recently the birds have discovered that human structures, like bridges, road culverts, and the eaves of people's houses, are better places to live, probably because nests there are less likely to be destroyed by storms and might be harder for predators to reach.

The center of the cliff swallow's universe in Nebraska (and probably the entire world) is the area around Keystone, just east of Kingsley Dam in Keith County. Here, the University of Nebraska's Cedar Point Biological Station is situated, surrounded by dozens of swallow colonies and thousands of nesting birds. In the summer of 2009 I estimated over forty-one thousand active cliff swallow nests between Maxwell, in Lincoln County, on the east and Broadwater, in Morrill County, to the west. Even before people built roads and bridges in Nebraska, these birds were reported to be nesting in the Platte Valley: naturalist-surgeons with the US Army found them on cliffs in the Ash Hollow area as early as 1845. To paraphrase the California ornithologist and swallow enthusiast William Dawson from 1923, the species' overwhelming abundance in the area around Keystone and Lake McConaughy makes it difficult to notice any birds there except cliff swallows! Providing a natural laboratory for the study of animal social life, this concentration of swallows drew me to the biological station almost thirty years ago, where I have since spent each summer trying to understand this bird's complex and fascinating social behavior.

## Benefits and Costs of Social Life

Many kinds of animals live in groups of different sizes during at least part of the year. Natural historians dating back to Aristotle have speculated on the advantages of living in close proximity to others of your ilk, but the modern study of animal sociality began only about forty years ago when biologists John Crook, David Lack, Hans Kruuk, Henry Horn, Richard Alexander, John Hoogland, and others adopted an evolutionary perspective on the formation of animal groups. They pointed out that there are both advantages and disadvantages to grouping. To understand why group life evolves in some species and not in others one must observe how the positive and negative factors interact to affect the animals' survival and reproduction.

Working on colonially nesting bank swallows (*Riparia riparia*) in Michigan, Hoogland and collaborator Paul Sherman were among the first scientists to measure how the costs and benefits of social living differed among birds living in colonies of different sizes. They found, for instance, that bank swallows in bigger colonies were parasitized by more blood-sucking fleas than those in small groups, yet the birds in the large colonies were more successful at thwarting attacks of predatory birds. The net gain seemed to favor bank swallows that formed colonies.

In 1982, when I first came to western Nebraska to study cliff swallows, we still had only a partial idea of what the different costs and benefits of living in colonies for birds might be. Some ecologists, like Hoogland and Sherman, felt that group living was most important in helping animals avoid being preyed upon: the more members in a group, the more "eyes" looking out for predators and thus a lower likelihood of getting eaten. Other scientists, like Amotz Zahavi, Stephen Emlen, and John Krebs, believed that animals formed groups mainly to aid in the search for food, particularly when the animals feed on patchy or ephemeral resources. Simply put, if it takes a long time to find a food source (such as a school of fish in the sea or a swarm of insects in the air), individuals can avoid the costs in time and energy of searching for food themselves by instead watching where others in that group feed and then following suit.

Yet despite these advantages to being together, a substantial disadvantage to social life is the increased likelihood of contracting parasites or disease from other group members through intentional or unintentional physical proximity and contact. The rampant spread of flu and other infectious diseases among college kids cooped up in large dormitories in the winter attests to this reality. It's now generally thought that all animals must pay this cost to some degree. Another universal drawback to social life is greater competition for resources. When many individuals of the same species all live together, they will likely eat the same foods or nest in the same kinds of places. This may force them to invest more time and energy in finding and defending food or nest sites from each other, or it may require them to travel farther in search of these commodities.

## Swallow Bugs and Social Foraging

My collaborator and fellow behavioral ecologist Mary Bomberger Brown, now at the University of Nebraska-Lincoln, and I quickly discovered in our research that the cliff swallows of the Platte Valley experience one classic cost of group living, an increased incidence of ectoparasites. The swallow bug (*Oeciacus vicarius*), a blood-sucking relative of the human bedbug, is adapted specifically to cliff swallows, and populations of these bugs can be quite large in swallow colonies (up to 2,600 bugs in a single nest). The bugs live in the swallows' nests or in cracks and crevices of the nesting substrate near the nests and feed on both the adult birds and the nestlings inside the nest.

We found that cliff swallow nests in larger colonies contained more bugs per nest than did those in smaller colonies. Furthermore, by fumigating nests with insecticide and removing the bugs in some nests, we found that bugs exert a severe cost to cliff swallows in larger colonies: Nestlings exposed to the many swallow bugs there often die before fledging, likely because of blood loss. Those that do survive to leave the nest are in poorer condition and less likely to live to return to Nebraska from

South America the next year. Sometimes bugs are so numerous in a colony that the cliff swallows there abandon it entirely, leaving their eggs or small nestlings to starve. (If swallows live on your property, have no fear: The bugs feed only on birds!)

With such a terrible price to pay for living together, swallows must gain some advantage from this lifestyle. The primary one, we believe, is the opportunity to use other colony members to help with finding food. In the early 1970s it was suggested that bird colonies might serve as "information centers," where birds could always reliably identify other members of the group who were knowledgeable at that moment as to the whereabouts of food. This would be particularly important if the species fed on food types that were unpredictable in where and when they could be found. Cliff swallows feed on swarms of insects concentrated in thermals of warm air that vary considerably in location over the course of even a single morning, and thus we knew early on that they would be good candidates for their colonies serving as information centers. I remember the very first morning in 1982 that I spent watching cliff swallows forage. I could tell immediately that group foraging was important for these birds, as solitary foragers were almost nonexistent and flocks stayed together cohesively as they looked for insects.

Mary and I subsequently verified that the swallows frequently observed others at a colony and learned who had been recently successful the same way we did: by seeing who came back with a beakful of insects to feed their babies. Birds who came back to their nests without food, the presumably unsuccessful ones, watched their neighbors, and when a nearby bird came back with food, the unsuccessful bird followed the successful one when it next left the colony to return to the food source. In this way, birds save the time and energy of hunting for the swarms, and the more birds present, the more quickly individuals can locate somebody who happens to know where the food is at any given time. This increased foraging efficiency compensates somewhat for the costs of bug parasitism in the larger colonies.

We discovered other advantages and disadvantages of social life. For example, birds in larger colonies are more likely to detect incoming hawks or snakes that prey on them. With all the closely spaced neighboring nests in larger colonies, birds' nests can share common walls, and this reduces the time and effort of building a nest. Cliff swallows have to travel farther to feed as colonies grow, however, because the many birds present tend to deplete the insects near a colony. Birds in larger colonies also fight more as they compete for the best places to build their nests (typically toward the center of the colony). The net effect of all the different costs and benefits of social life seems to be that in some years, cliff swallows nesting in large colonies have higher survival and raise more young, whereas in other years birds in medium-sized or small colonies have the advantage.


## Do unto Others before They Do unto You

The cliff swallow's highly social nature also illustrates a fundamental consequence of living together for most animals: There are plenty of opportunities to exploit others around you. By color-marking cliff swallows and intensively observing them at their nests, we discovered that these birds are constantly trying to use their neighbors to their own selfish advantage. A bird will intrude into the nest next door, steal its neighbor's nesting material (grass stems) or the wet mud on its nest, attempt to copulate with its neighbor's mate, throw out one of its neighbor's eggs, or in some cases even lay an egg in its neighbor's nest. These are not cases of mistaken nest identity, as cliff swallows clearly know whose nest is whose. Sometimes these trespass attempts are almost continuous, as birds repeatedly try to enter several of their neighbors' nests in rapid succession. Typically, cliff swallows guard their nests almost constantly, probably to try to prevent their neighbors from doing these things to them, but there are enough lapses in guarding that bad things do happen. Often one bird will steal grass from its neighbor only to have that neighbor return the favor at a later time; I once watched what looked like the same grass stem change "hands" several times as it was repeatedly stolen from a nest and then stolen back.

Probably the most unique way that cliff swallows exploit others is by foisting some of their eggs off onto their neighbors. Mary and I discovered relatively early in our research that these birds are like other species in that they sometimes lay eggs in the nests of other colony members. Typically, a female finds a neighboring nest unattended, slips in and lays an egg, and the unsuspecting neighbor is none the wiser. This enables the parasitic bird to then lay an additional egg in her own nest, and in that way increase her reproductive output. It also "spreads the risk" by not putting all her eggs in the same nest, should her own nest be depredated or be washed away by a storm. Up to 20 percent of swallow nests have parasitic eggs laid in them, and the odds of both finding a nest to parasitize and having your own nest victimized increase in larger colonies.

But cliff swallows have evolved an even neater trick to parasitize their neighbors. If you lay a parasitic egg, you have to time the laying to coincide with when your neighbor lays her eggs. Lay too early and the neighbor won't be at the appropriate stage to care for (incubate) the eggs. Lay too late and the neighbor's own eggs will have a head start in development and hatch before yours. This means parasitic laying is only possible during a fairly narrow window of time (three to four days). Yet if you *carry* an egg already laid in your own nest into a neighbor's, you have a longer window of time (the entire sixteen-day incubation period) to find your neighbor's nest left unguarded. Cliff swallows do just that. They physically transfer eggs in their beaks from their own nests into ones nearby. They even seem to be able to predict (how we don't know) which nests in the colony are less likely to have lots of swallow bugs, and eggs are transferred into those nests at a higher frequency than into the more infested nests. In this way, females seem to ensure that at least some of their offspring are reared in nests with fewer bugs and are thus more likely to survive.

## Why Colonies Vary in Size

One big reason that the cliff swallows of the Platte Valley have proven to be such marvelous research subjects is that they live in colonies that vary so much in size. A few birds are found each year that live by themselves, and others form colonies containing up to six thousand nests on a single bridge. Colonies spanning this entire range are found every year, with most birds living in groups of several hundred nests. This variation, which I was unaware of when I selected Keith County as a research site, has allowed us to study not only how the costs and benefits of social life vary with group size but also what ecological conditions might cause colonies to differ in size in the first place. This is a fundamental question about animal behavior but, surprisingly, one that has not been widely addressed.

One factor that determines, in part, the number of cliff swallows at a given colony site (e.g., on a particular bridge) is the nature of the habitat surrounding it. Feeding on small, swarming insects, the swallows prefer areas that support large numbers of swarms. Insect abundance and distribution is influenced by the type of vegetation, land use, and amount of water within the birds' foraging range. Sites that have a moderate amount of water (ponds, rivers, canals) relatively close and also have diversity in other kinds of habitat are the ones that support the largest swallow colonies. Sites surrounded by all of one kind of habitat (e.g., a cornfield) tend not to regularly attract as many birds, probably because there isn't enough insect food in the vicinity. The overall land use in the Platte Valley, with moderate amounts of standing or flowing water plus a mixture of cropland, prairie, riparian woodland, and town-like areas, probably accounts for the high abundance of cliff swallows in this area, simply because conditions are so good for insects.

Perhaps the most surprising single discovery about cliff swallows in the last twenty-eight years is the realization that colony size is, in part, based on genetics. It is well known that some animals produce increased levels of stress hormones in social situations, and some fifteen years ago I guessed that cliff swallows might "perform" better (i.e., be more successful in raising young) when in groups of particular sizes. Few colleagues, however, thought that an individual's choice of what size group it would live in could be determined by genes.

To determine if there were innate preferences for groups of particular sizes, we performed an experiment in which some nestlings born in a colony of one size were raised in a colony of a very different size. We had monitored when nestling cliff swallows hatched, and as soon as they were old enough (three to four days), we banded them for permanent identification. We then switched some babies born in large colonies to nests in small colonies to be raised by foster parents; we did the reverse with additional hatchlings.

If the babies' subsequent choice of where to live was based largely on genetic tendencies, the youngsters should later choose colonies that matched in size where they were born (where their parents chose to live), not where they were reared. On the other hand, if early experience as a fledgling in a particular social environment dictated later choices, the exchanged birds should choose colonies that matched the size of the sites where they were reared. The next summer we caught breeding birds, looking to see where our experimental birds returned and what size colonies they chose as first-time breeders. Yearling cliff swallows chose breeding colonies that matched in size with where they were born and rarely occupied sites similar to where they were reared. Thus, cliff swallows seem genetically programmed to use colonies of a particular size, and this accounts in part for the diversity of colony sizes seen in the population along the Platte River.

Although unappreciated by most people and certainly ignored by the many tourists cruising across Interstate 80 each summer, the cliff swallows of western Nebraska have provided insights that have reshaped the way scientists think about group living in animals. They are a fascinating treasure that everyone who lives in the state should protect and take the opportunity to enjoy.

# The Greater Prairie-chicken

*Spirit of the Tallgrass Prairie*

*By* PAUL A. JOHNSGARD

I saw my first greater prairie-chicken during the late 1930s, when I was about eight years old. It was only a freshly killed carcass, a result of a day of pheasant hunting by my father. He had hunted in an area of tallgrass prairie near my mother's girlhood home along the Sheyenne River in southeastern North Dakota and had never before shot a prairie-chicken. That area, now part of the Sheyenne National Grassland, was by then virtually the last place in North Dakota where prairie-chickens were still surviving in good numbers. I studied the bird's beautiful buff and burnt umber plumage carefully, thinking I might never see another. And, in fact, I did not see another until more than twenty years later when I moved to Nebraska and began a university teaching career lasting four decades. During that period I made it my sacred duty to never let a spring pass without spending at least one sunrise surrounded by male prairie-chickens performing their courtship rituals amid the previous year's growth of native prairie grasses. I knew I was witnessing a rare sight, as old as the glacier-shaped hills around me and as entrancing as a ballet performance of "Swan Lake." It always was a time of spiritual renewal for me, a recognition that, in the face of diminishing habitats, polluted environments, and declining populations, the birds were carrying on with all the determination and energy that a forty-five-ounce bird can muster.

Beyond the sheer beauty of the event, prairie-chicken courtship is a powerful symbol of the results of natural selection in shaping the appearance and behavior of grassland grouse. This species, like its near relative the lesser prairie-chicken and its slightly more distant cousin the sharp-tailed grouse, has placed all its reproductive strategies in a complex game of behavior called lekking. The winner determines which male in a local population has the stamina and experience to best all the other local males in a contest of physical strength and relative sexual attraction sufficient to claim mating rights to all the females in the vicinity.

Lekking behavior (the word is derived from a Scandinavian term meaning "to playfully flirt") is a mixture of threats, fights, and advertising one's maleness by visual and acoustic means. It is not unlike typical barroom behavior by men, with females being attracted to the most dominant individual. And, like most athletic events, lekking behavior occurs on traditional local gathering places called leks. There, suitable landscape features are present, such as hilltops that are free of trees and shrubs and where panoramic visibility is present so that any gate-crashers (predators) are likely to be detected from afar. Like human athletes, successful male grouse are likely to bear the scars of battle such as lost feathers, scratches, and occasional serious injuries. But, also like some athletes and entertainers, they enjoy only a year or two "at the top" for the privilege of spreading their genes widely through the local population. For prairie-chickens, it typically requires three years for a male to gain the strength and experience to outperform all the competing males. These "master cocks" are likely to be dead within a year or two later, but their widespread genes are likely to persist.

The major male lek display is called "booming," during which the sides of the male's neck are expanded by filling the esophagus with air, inflating two large, orange-colored "air sacs." This large air chamber serves as a resonating chamber for the associated vocalization, a low-pitched and dove-like call sounding like "Old Mul-doon." Although soft, the harmonic-rich call may be heard a mile or so away under favorable conditions. This powerful acoustic and visual signal is strong enough to attract all adult females within sight or hearing range, much like a rock band might attract crowds. Somehow, even under the dim light of dawn, females can identify the most virile male by his favored central position, his frequency of display, or his obvious social dominance and will selectively mate with him. Most studies of prairie-chickens have shown that at least 80 percent of all lek matings are performed by this master cock. Little if any mating occurs away from leks.

Clearly, the relative position of a male on a lek is an index to his relative social status. Prairie-chicken leks in Nebraska may have as few as four males but more often consist of a dozen or so. I have seen leks with up to forty-four males present, with as many as four or more females near the dominant male, waiting to be mated. First-year males on large leks are likely to be confined to peripheral locations, but by the time they are two years old they have probably graduated to more interior sites. There they are closer to the "action," and perhaps slightly safer from any predators successfully reaching the perimeter of the lek. Most master cocks of larger leks are likely to be at least three years old and have endured countless fights—unlike inheritance mechanisms in humans, there is no way to succeed in the lekking business without really trying. Master cocks tend to be in excellent physical condition, with high testosterone levels and very large testes.

The importance of master cocks in maintaining efficient reproduction in prairie-chickens was shown in a Kansas experiment, when the master cocks were selectively removed from leks during the height of the breeding season. The lek was immediately thrown into chaos, with no male able to attain master cock status that spring, and few if any matings occurred. No females were attracted the following year, and the lek was eventually abandoned.

After a female has been mated, and a singe mating provides each female with enough sperm to fertilize a clutch of a dozen or so eggs, she leaves the lek and selects a nest site, usually within a mile of the lek. She then lays her eggs, one per day, and begins the twenty-four- to twenty-five-day incubation period. The female alone undertakes all of the incubation and the later care for her chicks. She tends to the chicks until they fledge and for a while afterwards, but family groups gradually merge to form fall flocks. During fall, some of the males return to their lek to reclaim their old territories or try to establish a more favorable location closer to the lek center.

Americans are very lucky to have more species of lek-forming grouse to watch than anywhere else in the world, and all occur in open habitats where they can be easily watched. Besides the two prairie-chickens and the sharp-tailed grouse, there are also two species of sage grouse, whose leks typically have the largest number of males and the most complex courtship rituals. Sharp-tailed grouse are still fairly common over much of western Nebraska, especially in the Sandhills. Lesser prairie-chickens can still be seen at a few regional locations as close as the Cimarron National Grassland in southwestern Kansas, and numerous greater sage grouse leks are present on the vicinity of Laramie and Casper, Wyoming. The other sage grouse, the Gunnison, is an endangered species that is limited to southern Colorado and for various reasons is extremely difficult to observe.

## References

Johnsgard, P. A. *Grouse and Quails of North America*. Lincoln, NE: University of Nebraska Press, 1973. Available online at http://digitalcommons.unl.edu/bioscigrouse/1.

Johnsgard, P. A. *Grassland Grouse and Their Conservation*. Washington, DC: Smithsonian Institute Press, 2002.

Johnsgard, P. A. "The Drums of April." *Prairie Fire*, April 2010, 12-13. http://www.prairiefirenewspaper.com/2010/04/the-drums-of-april.

Paothong, N. and J. Vance. *Save the Last Dance: A Story of North American Grassland Grouse*. Published by N. Paothong, 2012.

# The Special Magic of Cranes

*By* GEORGE ARCHIBALD

Most springs during the past three decades I have been joined along the Platte River by a group of staff and members of the International Crane Foundation to experience one of earth's great spectacles—the gathering of perhaps more than a half-million sandhill cranes. The dean of Nebraskan ornithology, Dr. Paul Johnsgard, writes beautifully about the special magic that happens when in spring the Platte River and the sandhill cranes meet.

There is a magical time that occurs each year in the heart of North America, when the river and the season and the bird all come into brief conjunction.

I always anticipate "the wave" that sometimes happens at dawn when the shallows near Kearney are carpeted by cranes. The cranes stand silent in the cold, often one leg buried in warm breast feathers and beak tucked behind a folded wing. A distant and continuous roar tells that perhaps a bald eagle has scared up cranes. The bellow grows louder as the lifting of cranes spreads along the roosts like the wave of fans in a sports arena. Soon one is in the midst of the deafening voices of thousands of cranes. As the cranes disappear over the trees and the wave of rising cranes continues along the river, the roar fades.

The Platte River provides safe roosting places at night for the cranes, and the nearby cornfields offer an abundance of gleanings that help build fat reserves to fuel the cranes to complete migrations thousands of miles north. The cranes must take care not to fly into winter, so flight schedules are critical. And the great hordes of cranes attract human crane watchers from far and wide. It's a North American experience akin in splendor to the migrations of mammals on the plains of Africa.

## Ancient Birds

The sandhill is the most abundant of the world's fifteen species of cranes, and its ecological counterpart, the Eurasian crane, is a close second. Both nest primarily at high latitudes of the northern hemisphere where there are fewer humans. Studies of the anatomy, behavior, and DNA of cranes imply that the sandhill is perhaps the ancestor of a group of eight other species of cranes within the genus *Grus*. Only found in the New World, the closest relative to cranes, the limpkin, suggests that sandhills originated in North America, colonized Asia, and gave rise to other species including the Eurasian. Comparative studies clearly hint

178

that the closest relative of the rarest of cranes, the whooping crane of North America, is the Eurasian crane. Perhaps a group of Eurasian cranes colonized North America, discovered their preferred habitats filled with sandhills, and eventually evolved into a larger species that occupied deeper wetlands not used by sandhills.

Three crane species that depend on large wetlands, the whooping, the red-crowned, and the Siberian, are white. White-naped and wattled cranes have white necks and are also dependent on large wetlands. White stands out against a background of browns, greens, and blues in wetlands. Being obvious helps proclaim ownership of real estate that is critical for successful breeding. In contrast, cranes like sandhills and Eurasians that nest on smaller wetlands and that forage in nearby upland areas are gray and more difficult to see. Immediacy to uplands means proximity to predators. Feather painting in spring with iron-rich mud permanently stains the feathers of sandhills a reddish brown, rendering them even more difficult to see on their nests.

White cranes on large wetlands encounter more problems when faced with a human competitor than do less conspicuous cranes on smaller and more abundant wetlands. In the prime nesting areas of the whooping cranes—wetlands of the tall-grass prairie that stretched from the Midwest to southern Saskatchewan—hunting by subsistence pioneers from Europe and then the drainage of wetlands to create the world's food basket spelled the demise of the white cranes, while small and widely scattered groups of gray cranes survived.

## The Sandhills that Migrate to Nebraska

North of the prairies, sandhills from the boreal forests and tundras of the north survived in great numbers. During the past decade, by capturing twenty to thirty sandhills each spring in Nebraska, then measuring them, collecting blood and swabs, and attaching tiny radio transmitters that communicate with satellites, my colleagues from the Northern Prairie Research Center in Jamestown, North Dakota, have made some fascinating discoveries about the cranes that stop in Nebraska.

Most of the cranes rest along the sixty-mile west-to-east section of the Platte River roughly between the towns of North Platte and Grand Island. They can be divided into two distinct subspecies, the lesser sandhill, predominantly to the west, and the greater sandhill, predominantly to the east, with plenty of overlap in between. The lesser sandhills migrate to nest on the tundra from the west side of the Hudson Bay to Alaska and then up to 1,600 miles into eastern Russia. The greater sandhills are significantly larger than the lessers, and within their wide range from the boreal forests to the prairies, gradually change from small greaters in the north to larger birds in the south. Subspecies recognition in Nebraska is facilitated by looking at heads. The beak of the lesser is about the same length as the head, while the beak of the southern greater is almost twice the length of the head. Then to add to the challenge of identification, there is the small greater that is intermediate!

And while the sandhills gather in Nebraska in huge numbers in March waiting for spring farther north, in autumn they fly quickly across the tundra and boreal forest to wheat fields in southern Saskatchewan, where they spend several weeks to build up fat-fuel for a rapid migration to their wintering grounds in southwestern US and northern Mexico. In autumn they quickly fly across Nebraska, stopping occasionally just to rest at night.

## Whooping Cranes

The spring migration of whooping cranes, although following the same corridor as the sandhills, differs in timing. While sandhills spend several weeks to more than a month in Nebraska in March, the whooping cranes remain on their wintering grounds along the coast of Texas until early April and then fly directly to the breeding grounds in northern Canada, stopping only briefly to rest on wetlands and feed before, depending on the weather, mounting the mid-day thermals to continue their passage. But like the sandhills, in the fall the whooping cranes fly from the breeding areas across the boreal forests to the wheat fields of Saskatchewan, where they usually remain for more than a month before continuing as quickly as possible to the coastal wetlands of the Aransas National Wildlife Refuge.

While adult whooping cranes are white, post-fledged juveniles are cinnamon brown, making it easy to recognize families and to accurately document productivity. Winter counts in early winter in Texas indicate that on the average 12 percent of the birds are juveniles. By spring the young cranes are white. By counting the numbers that leave the wintering grounds and those that return, researchers have documented that about

8 percent of the cranes are lost between April and December, leaving just a 4 percent gain. However, during a recent winter drought in Texas, 9 percent of the cranes disappeared, presumably to starvation and associated predation. Fresh-water inflow from the Guadelupe-San Antonio River helps maintain the proper salinity of coastal wetlands for blue crabs, the most important food of whooping cranes in winter. Now there are concerns that overuse of the waters of the Guadelupe for cities, crops, nuclear power plants, and other applications will lead to increased salinity of coastal wetlands and a decline of crabs. The survival of the whooping crane remains fragile.

The International Crane Foundation, a nongovernmental organization headquartered in Baraboo, Wisconsin, works with contemporaries in Canada and the US to aid the whooping cranes, as well as with colleagues in Africa and Asia to help ten other species of threatened cranes. The opening of the heart of North America to European settlers almost caused the extinction of whooping cranes. Now the burgeoning human populations and demands for increased standards of living exert unprecedented pressures on cranes in the developing world, especially in sub-Saharan Africa and in southern Asia.

## Help for Cranes Worldwide

ICF holds that human values are the fundamental ingredients for conservation. If people care, they will help. In each of the places we work, ICF strives to get to know the local people, to listen to them, to help them with basic needs, and to identify key individuals within their ranks who have the leadership qualities and enthusiasm to help achieve win-win conservation solutions for both people and cranes. Helping maintain the spectacle of more than a half-million cranes in Nebraska is predicated on the goodwill of the farmers. Saving the flows of the Guadelupe-San Antonio River to help assure crabs for the whooping cranes depends on the values of Texans, especially those within the watershed and coastal outflow areas of the river. Helping the cranes in the developing world is dependent on finding solutions that meet basic human needs as well.

As so beautifully demonstrated in Nebraska each spring, when thousands of people meet hundreds of thousands of cranes, that harmony can be achieved.

# The Allure of Cranes

*By* PAUL A. JOHNSGARD

As a child growing up in a tiny North Dakota village, there were few ways to escape the confines of that whistle-stop hamlet. One was to walk the railroad track that went north toward Fargo, where I was born, or south toward places that were completely unknown to me. Walking these tracks allowed me to find wildflowers growing among the prairie grasses along the railroad right-of-way and to see birds like red-winged blackbirds as well as then-unidentifiable and still unidentified sparrows lurking in the tall ragweeds growing along the tracks.

Another escape consisted of watching the wavering formations of migrating white geese that every April flew over our house in countless numbers, headed for destinations that were far beyond my ken, both geographically and ecologically. Eventually I learned the birds were snow geese headed for the tundras of the high Canadian arctic. However, nearly three decades would pass before I was able first to set foot on that tundra and could wander ecstatically about a colony of nesting snow geese that stretched widely along the high-tide line of the vast Hudson Bay lowlands.

I then imagined that I could never be happier than to be surrounded by nesting geese, and more generally to observe wild geese, swans, and ducks. This became an obsession during college, and by the time I arrived in Lincoln, Nebraska, in 1961 I had been able to observe and study the comparative social behavior of more than 120 of the nearly 150 world waterfowl species. At that time I believed I would spend the rest of my life seeking out the remaining species, most of which were rarely observed ducks occurring in remote parts of the globe.

All that changed one fateful day in March 1962 when, with my first class of ornithology students, I ventured out to the central Platte Valley, hoping to see wild sandhill cranes for the first time in my life. After getting to Elm Creek on US Highway 30, without having seen any cranes, I decided to turn south toward a bridge over the Platte. Crossing that bridge was like landing in Oz, for on the other side were seemingly endless flocks of sandhill cranes feeding in the wet meadows. At that moment of epiphany the world suddenly shifted permanently for me; here were countless birds possessing all the visual beauty of geese, and additionally they had clarion voices that penetrated the brain in such a way as to haunt my memory permanently.

There are no words adequate to describe the voice of the sandhill crane; it has an authenticity that reflects immeasurable years of history, merged with a contemporary insistence that demands one's immediate attention. It carries across both miles of space and eons of time, linking those lucky enough to hear it with both the distant past and the present, and human-kind with the natural world.

I then realized that I must always have the voices of cranes in my memory and try to renew their sounds at every opportunity. Since then I have seen all fifteen species of cranes, each as fascinating as the sandhill and all far less common, some indeed now living in the shadow of extinction.

In North America these species include the whooping crane, an even larger and immaculate white bird with black wing-tips, possessing a trumpeting voice far more powerful than the sandhill's, and with a wild population that, when I was still a child in North Dakota, numbered less than two dozen birds in the world and was still a bird of mystery. In the seventy years since then their numbers in the wild have reached over three hundred, their subarctic Canadian nesting grounds have been discovered, and dozens of research papers and theses have been written on their biology.

On that memorable March day in 1962 we stayed until sunset, hunkered down in high weeds along the river, breathlessly watching the procession of cranes passing majestically above us in the fading light as they circled and glided down into a mid-river roosting place. Thereafter, for nearly four decades I made the same Mecca-like pilgrimage with my ornithology classes each March, hoping that the crane's magic would shape and transform the students as it did me. Indeed, many of them went on to become experts in crane biology, and I believe all of them were touched deeply by the experience.

Cranes are so graceful and beautiful in flight that, when watching them, I sometimes wonder if I am seeing apparitions or real birds. In many ways they also remind us of humans in their social structure and basic biology. Their life spans are potentially as long as a human's, and they form strong pair bonds that are likely to be broken only through the death of a mate or the pair experiencing an initial breeding failure. Although most cranes normally lay two eggs and the young are cared for by both parents, the second-laid and second-hatched youngster only infrequently survives long enough to attain flight. In another human-like aspect, there is a strong sibling rivalry for food and attention. The younger and weaker chick may die of the resulting stress and parental inability to care adequately for both young. By the time the birds migrate south through Nebraska, less than 10 percent of the flock consists of juveniles. Even fewer are present when the birds return north in spring. At that time the young birds are starting to shed their gray crown feathers, exposing bare red skin, and their voices are shifting from a high-pitched whistle to lower, more throaty, and much more powerful notes as their windpipes lengthen to generate the harmonic-rich acoustics typical of adults.

Those youngsters that do live to fledging age (at about two-and-one-half months) are taught to fly through repeated training flights by both parents, during which the youngsters no doubt learn the area's local geography. They later accompany their parents on the long seasonal migrations to and from wintering areas; over the course of several years of learning landmarks as they progress toward sexual maturity, they too eventually become experts at international or even intercontinental navigation.

Sandhill crane flocks are often astonishingly large, sometime numbering in the thousands of birds, but pairs and families are able to remain connected by maintaining contacts with other family members through individual acoustic or visual recognition. These conversational communications of flying cranes are critical for reestablishing social bonds, especially after roosting flocks are startled and put to flight. Sometimes, after the flock has settled again, a single bird will fly up and down the river calling in search of its mate or parents, as plaintively as would a lost child. At such times it becomes clear that a crane society is fragile and that to disrupt it in such a way (by excessive disturbance or, worse yet, by hunting) that family or pair bonds are irrevocably broken may cause far more damage than one might imagine.

Crane behavior is best observed from inside a car or, better yet, a blind. It is then, when the birds are at ease, that one can begin to understand the complexity of their social structure. At various times crane "dancing" might be seen; it is a combination of jumping, wing flapping, head bowing, and object tossing, as well as the circling of one partner by the other or a single bird rotating in place while lifting its wings. Dancing during spring migration is usually sporadic and the movements are not as fully developed as on the breeding grounds. Elements of dancing may also be elicited during disturbance or antagonistic interactions between flock members; thus dancing during migration probably has little relationship to courtship but may be of substantial importance in pair-bond maintenance.

Also of great importance to maintenance of pair bonds in all crane species is the "unison call." During migration, it most often occurs after some activity that upsets the normal peaceful situation, such as an intrusion into the personal space of another pair member or the pecking of one individual by another. The two pair or potential pair members then call jointly in a loud duet. Both birds utter a long series of uniformly spaced notes, the male uttering single notes and the female a similar series of double notes. In addition to their vocal differences, the male tilts his beak vertically and stretches his neck higher and farther back while calling, while the female typically tilts her head at a diagonal angle and exhibits less extreme neck stretching. This intense interaction seems to be of central importance in pair-bond formation and maintenance.

The language of crane social behavior is a complex subject, and one might spend years, if not a lifetime, trying to understand it. It is a far more rewarding way of interacting with cranes than looking at them over the barrel of a shotgun.

# Monarch Butterflies

## The Last Migration

*By* Benjamin Vogt

---

On May 23 my wife yelled to me from the back door of our house: "There's a monarch on the allium!" The last two springs, this being our third here, we had not seen a monarch butterfly until around my birthday in mid-July. And frankly, I didn't expect to see hardly any this whole summer. As I dashed out to the garden with my camera in hand, there it was, fighting forty mph wind gusts, rising and slicing through the air to land on an allium, as bumblebees zipped around it like electrons. I knew the moment wouldn't last.

In 2007 my wife and I moved into our first home together, new construction on the edge of Lincoln. The holdout American elm in the corner of the quarter-acre lot had barbed wire still wound around its trunk, a property marker for some farmer's previous field. As a child, I tended her gardens with my mother in Minnesota, and as I grew older, confined to apartments, I knew I'd want a big garden someday. With a can of orange spray paint, and a day or two before the sod came in, I marked off two thousand feet of beds and borders for an ornamental garden designed specifically for native wildlife and plants. Milkweed was first on the list.

I actually knew little about gardening but meticulously researched Plains and Midwestern plants online, purchasing the right plant for the right spot—the dry hill and the mucky clay valley of my small yard. I dug ten dollar holes for one dollar plants from morning to sunset in ninety-degree heat for two summers. Some of the first plants were two *Asclepias incarnatas* (swamp milkweed) and an *Asclepias tuberosa* (butterfly weed), larval host plants for the monarch butterfly and named after the Greek god of healing, Asklepios. Milkweed is said to treat warts and poison ivy, remove mucus from the lungs, cool fevers, and work as a contraceptive. You never know how you might need your plants.

At night that first summer of gardening I'd dream of black-laced orange butterflies and dozens of other insects and birds frolicking in my Eden. But I didn't know what to expect. I was a book-reading graduate student, no botanist or entomologist. In 2008, when I noticed a yellow, white, and black striped caterpillar, I really had no idea it was a monarch until I did a Google search. I didn't know the thirty pen-tip-sized white pegs on the undersides of leaves were eggs that would hatch a few days after being laid. The monarchs had come like magic.

Folklore states that if a butterfly flies into your face, cold weather is imminent. For some, it means that within ten days sufficient frost will turn the leaves the same color as the butterfly. In central Mexico come fall, the monarch arrives, at the end of a three-thousand-mile migration from as far as southern Canada, on the Day of the Dead, which marks the return of a deceased loved one's soul. No one knows how these monarchs, several generations removed from their northward-bound ancestors, find their way back to their winter home.

The Mariposa Monarch Biosphere Reserve (138,000 acres) lies in the central Mexican states of Michoacan and Mexico. While Angangueo is considered the unofficial monarch headquarters, the most prominent overwintering site is in El Rosario, where as many as four million butterflies—of an estimated two hundred million—roost per acre in the fir and pine trees of the oyamel forests on only twelve mountaintops. The trees provide shelter from cold rains, which can freeze the monarchs, while they also hold in warmth rising from the forest floor. The conditions are precariously perfect, delicate microclimates, and only since 1975—as a result of ads taken out in Mexican newspapers—have scientists known the home location of the world's only migrating butterfly.

The summer breeding range of monarchs in the US east of the Rockies is over 247 million square acres, but in Mexico the insects cluster in only a few colonies that range in size from one to ten acres. Like massive dreadlocks, they hang from trunks and branches in suspended reproduction or diapause. These monarchs were born in September, and unlike the summer generations that live for only two to four weeks, they will last seven months until the February and March migration back north to Texas and the Gulf states, where they will lay eggs and quickly die.

How can an insect with the mass of a paperclip make such journeys and endure? As I watch the July monarchs perform aerial courting—the male dive-bombing and grabbing at the female, hoping to get her on the ground for copulation—I find it amazing that their four thin wings don't shred. In the heat, the wind, the miles of interstate, they dodge death. And then there are blue jays and orioles, who have learned to only eat the thoracic muscles to avoid the poisonous wings that contain cardenolides, which induce vomiting and heart attacks in predators. Tachnid flies lay eggs in caterpillars—maggots emerge weeks later from a newly formed chrysalis. An estimated 90 percent of monarch larvae never develop into butterflies, and the milkweed they depend upon in North America is quickly vanishing as six thousand acres per day of habitat is destroyed by human development.

Patches of milkweed are few and far between. Counties mow vital highway edges and destroy stands of milkweed and nectar plants. Farmers plant genetically modified corn and soybeans that are herbicide resistant, so chemicals like Roundup are liberally applied, easily killing any nearby milkweed. In Mexico between 1986 and 2006, one-fifth of the Monarch Biosphere—where only some of the winter roosts are located—was illegally logged, resulting in nearly twenty-six thousand acres of deforestation. How does the monarch persist?

In the winter of 2009-10, massive rain and hailstorms washed away local villages and monarch roosts in Mexico, resulting in an estimated 50-80 percent loss of the already record low 4.7 acres of monarchs, down from the average of 18 acres. In 1996 a record-high winter population was set at forty-four acres, but in 1997 the population was just fifteen acres. Again, from 1999–2000, the population went from twenty-two acres to seven acres, then in 2004 dropped to five acres.

The Commission for Environmental Cooperation does not list the monarch as endangered but does list the migration as such. Scientists agree that with shifting weather patterns due to global warming, the overwintering sites in Mexico will be uninhabitable by 2055 as the Mexican mountains experience more rain. But with the fragmented and vanishing stands of milkweed in North America, it maybe won't matter. In the spring of 2009 a dry Texas winter meant fewer milkweed for arriving monarchs, and a cold and wet Midwestern spring and summer slowed migration and inhibited milkweed growth.

But perhaps the monarch is just a butterfly, just one organism, just one phenomenon among thousands on the planet. Or maybe the potential disappearance of one species would diminish human culture itself—the Native American Pima tribe cite the creator as having taken the form of a butterfly, for example. The monarch has spread to Australia, Indonesia, the Azores, the Bahamas, and Spain through introduction, and the western population is relatively stable (and much smaller) as it migrates from British Columbia to southern California each year, so the monarch won't vanish entirely. But the metaphor their lives represent is obvious.

In Christianity the caterpillar's two weeks of life represents our earthly self, the chrysalis our tomb, the emergence (ten to fourteen days later for a monarch) is a casting off of our body and a spiritual rebirth. The monarch is more than a reminder of ourselves, it is the center of our moral and ethical beliefs as another species sharing and taking care of the Earth, and in turn ourselves. Organizations like Monarch Watch, MonarchLab, and the Commission for Environmental Cooperation are trying to make preservation and ecotourism a physically benign yet economically viable option for Mexicans who harvest the forest to heat homes, cook food, and just barely survive. These same organizations work in North America on a seemingly different level—to appeal to our humanity, our compassion, our sense of wonder and aesthetic joy.

Somewhere in the middle is the monarch butterfly. Somewhere in my garden now a female, slightly smaller than a male and missing two pheromone-producing androconium spots on two of its wings, may be laying eggs underneath milkweed leaves. She is tattered and faded, her short summer lifespan nearing an end, but a few of her four hundred eggs will emerge as an echo of herself in four weeks, a rebirth noticed by our own ancestors long ago—a symbol of defiance and hope in a new world more reminiscent of small, carefully tended gardens than of one vast nature.

- Peak fall migration in Nebraska: September 8-20
- Places to buy milkweed and nectar plants online: Prairie Nursery, Prairie Moon Nursery, Butterfly Encounters
- Key nectar plants: joe-pye weed, New England aster, goldenrod, ironweed, coneflower, pasture or field thistle, milkweed, Liatris (especially L. ligulystilis)
- Milkweed: Asclepias incarnata (swamp), A. sullivantii (sullivant's), A. purpurascens (purple)

- Monarch Watch: Register your garden as a Monarch Waystation, learn to raise and tag monarchs, read about monarchs aboard the International Space Station at http://monarchwatch.org
- Journey North: Track the monarch spring migration at http://learner.org/jnorth/monarch/

# Acknowledgments

The publishing of this book has been a long, strange trip indeed, and we would like to thank the people and organizations who helped a fledgling idea become a reality:

Jack Phillips, who started the whole thing and kept it going; Paul A. Johnsgard, who helped—tremendously; Tom Lynch, who gave generously of his time and talents; *Prairie Fire*, the regional monthly journal from Lincoln, Nebraska, without which these essays may not have been written or published; Cris Trautner and Aaron Vacin of Prairie Chronicles Press/Infusionmedia and *Prairie Fire*, who helped keep the fire burning; Rick Edwards, director of the Center for Great Plains Studies, who saw a good idea and a good purpose and funded it; the Great Plains Ecotourism Coalition, without which this book may not have seen light of day (or dark of night, for that matter).

There are twenty-four authors in this anthology and twenty-six essays. We wish to thank each and every one of these writers for first contributing to the *Prairie Fire* canon and now contributing to this anthology.

We would also like to thank Katie Nieland at the Center for Great Plains Studies for doing such an outstanding job on the map at the front of this book.

Finally, we would like to thank the thousands of readers and supporters of *Prairie Fire*. When the print edition went "on hiatus" for a few months, we heard nothing but good things about the paper, about what it does for the community, about how much it was missed, and we were humbled.

# About the Authors

We deeply appreciate the following writers' contributions to this anthology.

DR. GEORGE ARCHIBALD's visionary leadership in international conservation efforts over the past forty years has given flight to crane conservation worldwide. In 1973, when cranes were in a perilous situation and many were on the brink of extinction, Archibald, along with Cornell University colleague, Ronald Sauey, established the International Crane Foundation in Baraboo, Wisconsin, as the world center for the study and preservation of cranes. Archibald is a true conservation ambassador who uses his unique brand of crane diplomacy to work in sensitive places in over forty-five countries, currently Bhutan, China, India, North Korea, South Korea, Thailand, Japan, England, Ethiopia, Mongolia, and Russia. In recognition of his accomplishments, Archibald has received many awards and honors, including the Gold Medal from the World Wildlife Fund, MacArthur Foundation Fellows Award, Lilly Medal-Indianapolis Prize, and the inaugural Dan Lufkin Award.

ALAN J. BARTELS is a writer, photographer, student of nature, father, volunteer, and wanderer. At an early age he developed a love of all wild things, but since finding his first painted turtle at about age five, he has developed what he admits to be an abnormal fascination with turtles. In an effort to educate people about these often-overlooked creatures, he has given countless free educational programs, rehabilitated numerous sick and injured turtles, and has trapped, marked, radio tagged, and tracked turtles in an effort to further understand these amazing wonders of nature. Sandhill cranes, prairie-chickens, craft beers, and the Nebraska Sandhills are among his other loves. Bartels is a self-taught photographer and the assistant editor of *Nebraska Life Magazine*.

WILLIAM BEACHLY is a native of Lincoln, Nebraska, and has taught biology at Hastings College since 1996. He has been a contributor to *Prairie Fire* and *NEBRASKAland Magazine*. In the fall 2012 issue of *Humanimalia* he writes about a spider endemic to Lincoln that may have inspired Nebraska anthropologist and nature writer Loren Eiseley. He is currently working on a collection of essays about Nebraska's Outback.

CHARLES R. BROWN, professor of biological sciences at the University of Tulsa, has studied swallows since age eleven. Over the last thirty-three years in western Nebraska, he and a research team have banded more than 225,000 cliff swallows. Receiving degrees from Austin College (BA) and Princeton University (PhD), Brown published his first scientific paper at age fifteen, and his articles have appeared in *Nature, Science, Evolution, Ecology,* and many other publications. His book, *Swallow Summer,* was published by the University of Nebraska Press in 1998. In 2009 Brown and collaborator Mary Bomberger Brown of the University of Nebraska-Lincoln received the Elliot Coues Award from the American Ornithologists' Union in recognition of their outstanding research on cliff swallows.

In 2011 Brown received the Animal Behavior Society's Exemplar Award for his work on cliff swallows.

LINDA R. BROWN is a retired pharmacist who likes birds, prairies, and digital photography. She is a member of Wachiska Audubon.

SIBYLLA BROWN and her husband, Bill, moved from the city to their farm in Decatur County, Iowa. They had no idea that they would soon be restoring a degraded oak savanna. They began managing their property by thinning the overstocked oak and hickory woodland. Two years later they implemented prescribed burns to control the brush. Gradually their degraded woodland became high-quality oak savanna.

STEPHEN J. DINSMORE is currently employed as a wildlife ecologist (professor and associate department chair) in the Department of Natural Resource Ecology and Management at Iowa State University. He received a BS in fisheries and wildlife biology from Iowa State University (1990), a MS in zoology (minor in statistics) from North Carolina State University (1994), and a PhD in fishery and wildlife biology from Colorado State University (2001). His primary interests are avian ecology, population biology, capture-recapture analysis, and monitoring animal populations. His research program at Iowa State University emphasizes studies of avian population biology. He gives seminars and scientific presentations nationwide and enjoys teaching workshops on the use of Program MARK and the analysis of wildlife demographic data. In his spare time, he enjoys bird-watching and traveling.

DEB ECHO-HAWK is Keeper of the Seeds for the Pawnee Nation of Oklahoma Seed Preservation Project. Believing that the seeds that have sustained our Pawnee for hundreds of years should be a part of our daily diet, Echo-Hawk has worked with her brothers, Walter and Roger, family, and friends with consultation from the Nasharo Council of Chiefs and Pawnee Cultural Committee to preserve these seeds. The Seed Preservation Project is unique, including gardeners from the tribal homeland in Nebraska in addition to Oklahoma gardeners. Also unique is the DNA study of the corn seeds conducted by Nebraska volunteer Dr. Tom Hoegemeyer, chairman of the Technical Steering Group of US Germplasm Enhancement of Maize.

RICHARD EDWARDS, an economist, is director of the Center for Great Plains Studies, University of Nebraska. He founded the Great Plains Ecotourism Coalition in 2014; see http://www. visittheprairie.com or http://www.unl.edu/plains/ecotourism.

MICHAEL FARRELL practices the traditional craft of photography using large-format cameras and lenses, developing his own black-and-white negatives, and making enlargements in his darkroom or in color through digital scans and inkjet printing. His works spans the genres of landscape, still life, and nudes. He has had a professional career in documentary film and television production with many award-winning nationally and internationally distributed programs during his forty-five years in public broadcasting. He is a recipient of the Nebraska Arts Council's Individual Artist Fellowship in Visual Arts. His various one-person exhibitions have been included consistently in the top ten art events of the year by the Lincoln *Journal Star*.

MATT GERSIB is a Lincoln, Nebraska-based writer, cyclist, mentor, and business owner. In addition to owning a successful strategic communications firm, Gersib is the 2014 Gravel World Champion in the fatbike category and the 2012 Nebraska State Marathon Champion on the mountain bike. He also mentors youth through the TeamMates mentoring program and is a board member of the Nebraska Bicycling Alliance and Trails Have Our Respect.

TWYLA M. HANSEN, Nebraska's State Poet (2013-18), is the author of six books of poetry, including Nebraska Book Award-winning *Dirt Songs: A Plains Duet* (with Linda M. Hasselstrom) and *Prairie Suite: A Celebration* (with Paul Johnsgard). She is a creative writing presenter through Humanities Nebraska and Nebraska Arts Council. Her poetry and nonfiction prose have been published in periodicals, newspapers, anthologies, a textbook, *The Encyclopedia of the Great Plains*, *The Writers Almanac*, film-illustrated on NET Nebraska's *Next Exit*, transcribed for women's chorus, commissioned by National Arbor Day Foundation, and much more. She grew up on land in Burt County her grandparents farmed in the late 1800s as immigrants from Denmark. Her BS and MA are from the University of Nebraska-Lincoln, and she was employed for years in horticulture and organic agriculture certification. She is an associate fellow of the Center for Great Plains Studies and has served on several community and regional nonprofit boards. In 1972 she and her husband, Tom, built their home on an overgrazed pasture in northeast Lincoln and transformed the acre into a wooded urban wildlife habitat, winning the Mayor's Conservation Landscape Award in 1994.

CHRIS HELZER is an ecologist, photographer, and writer from Aurora, Nebraska. He is the eastern Nebraska program director for The Nature Conservancy and the author of the book *The Ecology and Management of Prairies in the Central United States* and the popular blog, The Prairie Ecologist.

John Janovy Jr. is professor emeritus at the University of Nebraska-Lincoln. He has published seventeen books and over one hundred scientific papers. Most of the books use nature to explore themes such as interdependency, intellectual freedom, testing one's limits and learning from the experience, creativity in teaching, and the development of careers, but some are fiction, including science fiction and mysteries. He taught, often to very large audiences, for forty-six years and won numerous teaching awards, including the University of Nebraska Distinguished Teaching Award, the Burlington-Northern Teacher-Scholar Award, the University of Nebraska Outstanding Research and Creativity Award, and the American Society of Parasitologists Clark P. Read Mentor Award. Presentation audios, PowerPoints, and a complete

CV can be found at http://www.johnjanovy.com. His blog is
http://fridaycoffee.blogspot.com.

PAUL A. JOHNSGARD is Foundation Professor of Biological Sciences Emeritus at the University of Nebraska. He received the Distinguished Teaching Award, Outstanding Research and Creative Activity Award, and an Honorary Doctor of Science degree from the university. He also was awarded a Guggenheim Foundation Fellowship, the National Wildlife Federation's National Conservation Achievement Award, the National Audubon Society's Charles H. Callahan Award, and the American Ornithologists' Union's Ralph Schreiber Conservation Award, all in recognition of his ornithological writing and conservation work. To date he has written 68 scholarly books, including 9 world avian monographs, plus 5 nontechnical or fictional books, more than 100 peer-reviewed articles, and about 150 nature-related popular articles, making him the world's most prolific author of ornithological literature.

TOM LYNCH is a professor in the English Department at the University of Nebraska-Lincoln, where he teaches ecocriticism and place-oriented literature. He is the coeditor of two recent books, *The Bioregional Imagination: Literature, Ecology, and Place* and *Artifacts and Illuminations: Critical Essays on Loren Eiseley.* He also serves as editor of the scholarly journal *Western American Literature.*

RONNIE O'BRIEN had worked at the Great Platte River Road Archway since its opening in 2000 at the time of writing for

*Prairie Fire.* As director of cultural education, she worked extensively to create programs and events based on the historic routes represented in the Archway and the people they impacted. Raised on a corn farm near Saint Libory, Nebraska, she feels the importance of involving fellow Nebraska gardeners to help return a staple crop to its people, the Pawnee.

MITCH PAINE currently works for the Nebraska Department of Natural Resources as the flood mitigation planning coordinator, where he coordinates activities to make communities safer and more resilient from flooding across the state. He previously worked for Lincoln Mayor Chris Beutler and helped start the city's environmental and sustainability program. Mitch is also an accomplished photographer, having covered the Keystone Pipeline, environmental campaigns, numerous congressional races, and endangered species like the Salt Creek tiger beetle. You can find his work at http://www.mitchpainephotography.com. He holds a master's degree in city planning from Cornell University and a bachelor's degree in economics from the University of Nebraska-Lincoln.

HEATHER SARLES PAYNE is the public information officer for the Otoe-Missouria Tribe. One of the goals of the office is to gather, preserve, and share historically important information and photos regarding the Otoe-Missouria people, culture, history, and language. To learn more about the Otoe-Missouria Tribe, visit www.omtribe.org.

JACK PHILLIPS is a naturalist with New Tree School and author of the expanded second edition of *The Bur Oak Manifesto: Seeking Nature and Planting Trees*, published by Prairie Chronicles Press.

JOANNA POPE is a public affairs officer with the USDA Natural Resources Conservations Service in Lincoln, Nebraska. She is a native Nebraskan who grew up in the Platte River Valley. After graduating from the University of Nebraska-Lincoln with a BS in environmental science, she began her career with NRCS and the Rainwater Basin Joint Venture as a conservationist. She now dedicates her time to telling the stories of the Nebraska landowners and operators who generously choose to conserve the natural resources on their property.

JOEL SARTORE, photographer and lifelong Nebraskan, brings a sense of humor and a Midwestern work ethic to all of his *National Geographic Magazine* assignments. Over twenty years of experience (more than fifteen with the National Geographic Society) have allowed him to cover everything from the remote Amazon rain forest to beer-drinking, mountain-racing firefighters in the United Kingdom. Besides the work he has done for *National Geographic*, Sartore has completed assignments for *Time, Life, Newsweek, Sports Illustrated,* and numerous book projects. Sartore and his work have been the subject of several national broadcasts, including National Geographic's *Explorer,* the NBC *Nightly News,* NPR's *Weekend Edition,* and CBS *Sunday Morning,* as well as an hour-long PBS documentary. Sartore is a National Geographic fellow and the founder of the Photo Ark. Prints and books by Joel Sartore are available at his website, www.joelsartore.com.

ROBERT KELLEY SCHNEIDERS, PhD, is an environmental consultant for Eco InTheKnow, LLC in Boulder, Colorado.

BENJAMIN VOGT owns Monarch Gardens, a prairie garden consulting and design firm. He writes a weekly native plant garden column at Houzz.com and is the author of several books while contributing to others, including a book on butterfly gardening from The Xerces Society and *Lawn Gone: Low Maintenance, Sustainable, Attractive Alternatives for Your Yard*. His poetry, nonfiction, and photography have appeared in dozens of publications including *Orion*, *The Sun*, and *Creative Nonfiction*, as well as the anthology *The Tallgrass Prairie Reader*. He has a PhD from the University of Nebraska and speaks nationally on pollinator gardens, ecological design, and the ethics of native plant landscapes in a time of climate change. Vogt shares his garden stories and philosophical musings at his blog, The Deep Middle, and champions pollinating insects at the Facebook page Milk the Weed.

## About the Great Plains Ecotourism Coalition

The Great Plains Ecotourism Coalition is committed to promoting environmental conservation and building thriving human communities through nature-based tourism in the Great Plains. The coalition includes both nonprofit and for-profit members and is coordinated by staff at the Center for Great Plains Studies at the University of Nebraska-Lincoln.

## Why Ecotourism?

Ecotourism is travel that deepens one's engagement with nature, conserves the environment, and improves the well-being of local communities. Ecotourism generates revenues critical for funding conservation initiatives, increases public awareness of and support for conservation, and helps nearby human communities thrive economically and culturally. All three of these elements are crucial to sustained and healthy conservation in the Great Plains. Ecotourism offers some of the most magical and inspiring moments of the human experience.

## Who Belongs to the Coalition?

Members include a variety of conservation and natural resources organizations and ecotourism businesses that support the overall mission of the coalition. Check the website for a list of current members.


## What Does the Coalition Do?

The coalition works to:

- Connect nature-based entrepreneurs with one another, creating opportunities for collaboration, learning, and cooperation.
- Market the region to ecotourists in the United States and beyond through targeted and creative advertising campaigns.
- Share information about ecotourism with participating members through a website, social media, and small conferences.
- Undertake or commission studies and research on ecotourism-related topics of substantial interest to members and ecotourists.
- Disseminate useful and reliable information of relevance to members.
- Engage in other activities to promote ecotourism in the Great Plains with the coalition members' support.